The Water-Babies
Tom becomes A Water-Baby

Illustrations by **Virginia Smith**
based on the Animation+Live Action film
The Water-Babies.
A Peter Shaw Production.

COLLINS COLOUR CUBS

If you know the story of Tom, the little chimney-sweep, you will know that when he plunged into the deep pool with his dog, Toby, they did not drown as the squire thought and the keeper thought and Tom's cruel master, Mr Grimes, thought and the little girl, Ellie, thought.

Tom was turned into a water-baby, his sooty skin washed quite clean.

Now I've no doubt you have been taught to swim. Toby could swim; but then dogs are clever creatures and can swim without being taught.

But Tom had spent all his life sweeping
chimneys in and around the busy, bustling
city and had never even seen the sea, let
alone learnt to swim.

At first he tried to walk but his feet danced away with him. And then he seemed to go sideways like a crab.

"Oh, I can't do it!" wailed Tom.

"He can't do it!" mocked the minnows in their shrill little voices. "What's the matter with you?"

"I can't swim," said Tom.

"Can't swim? But you're under water, aren't you?"

"But WHAT is he?" croaked three curious frogs.

"Yes, what ARE you?" asked the frogs and minnows all together.

"I'm Tom!"

"A tom? What's a tom?" boomed the eels.

"The trouble is he can't swim!" said the water-snails.

"Can't swim!" exclaimed the eels. "Oh!"

"No, I can't!" said Tom furiously.

"Queerest thing I ever heard!" said a water-rat. "If you can't swim . . ."

". . . you shouldn't be here!" they all chorused.

"Well, I AM and I CAN'T!" said Tom.

The water-rats crossed their legs and scratched their heads.

"The answer lies in teaching the Thing to swim," they announced.

"THING!" said Tom. "Don't call me a THING!"

"Watch!" said the frogs, swimming past.

"Watch!" said the minnows, swimming past.

"Watch!" said the eels, swimming past.

"And watch!" said the water-rats. "Rats swim BESTEST!"

Tom really tried, but he got tangled up in the reeds. "It's no good!" he said in despair. "I'll never be able to swim!"

"Absolute nonsense!" boomed two deep voices in high-falutin' tones.

Now after all this you won't be surprised to learn that one of the voices belonged to a lordly salmon who wore a monocle in his right eye and was known to all as Ralph.

And the other voice belonged to his haughty wife, Wilhelmina.

"All it takes is a little *perseverance*," she said.

"Clear a space!" boomed Ralph.

At once all the sea creatures began to spin and dart about in a flurry. They took turns to push and pull Tom into position for swimming.

Ralph and Wilhelmina swam around in
a stately sort of dance, singing:

> When you're sinking fast
> And you think you won't last
> Gotta try a little harder.

"Now try!" said Ralph to Tom, and the sea creatures sang to encourage him.

Come on try, come on try
Come on try, come on try
Come on try a little harder.

When you slip and slide
Gotta swallow your pride
And try a little harder.

Never say die
You know you'll get by
If you try . . . !

Never give in
And keep your chin
Right up high . . .!

'Cos it's no disgrace
When you fall on your face
Gotta try a little harder.

Though your backbone feels
Like a conger-eel's
C'mon try a little harder.

If you're in doubt
You've got to reach out
For a friend . . . !

Someone to share
And help you get there
In the end . . . !

When you've sunk so low
That there's no lower to go
Come on, try a little harder.

When things are looking dim
Get right back in the swim
And try a little harder.

"I can do it! I can *really* swim!" shouted Tom as he swam in time to the singing.

Come on try, come on try
Come on try, come on try
Come on try a little harder.

Tom had never had so much fun in his life before . . . until . . .

"OTTERS!" yelled one of the frogs.
"Swim for your lives!!!"

"Make for the weeds!" screamed the eels.

"Every fish for himself!" bellowed
Ralph. "Come along, my dear!"

And there they were. Three of the toughest, wildest-looking villains you ever saw.

"Food!" they yelled, darting in all directions. "Food! Food! Food!"

"What's wrong with everybody?" asked Tom in bewilderment.

"Make all speed, boy!" called Ralph, swimming past with Wilhelmina, two otters close behind.

"The fat one's mine!" yelled one of the otters.

The third otter had his eye on Tom.
And it wasn't exactly a friendly eye!
"I'm off!" said Tom.

"Come back, you!" yelled the otter.
Tom moved fast – but so did the otter!

Tom moved fast, but the otter moved
faster! Then he spotted Toby hiding
in a pile of old ginger-pop bottles.

BOP! BANG! CRASH!

The otter was tossing the bottles aside to get at Toby. But Tom was getting at *him*! He tied an old boat-paddle to the otter's tail.

WHAM!
As the otter turned and dived between the posts the paddle jammed and pulled him back with a WHACK!

"How's a chap supposed to have his dinner when his dinner won't fight fair?" he grumbled.

"Fight fair!" said Tom angrily. "What cheek!"

"Now you're insulting me!" said the otter.

"Well, are you going to leave me alone?" asked Tom.

"Who wants a skinny little newt anyway?" said the otter.

"I'm not a newt! I'm Tom and I belong Up There!" said Tom.

"You're a long way from home," said the otter.

Tom tried a little flattery.

"You're so smart, Mr Otter, I'm sure you could help me to get back."

"I've been thinking," said the otter, "you must be one of those water-babies. Now if you could find *them*, perhaps they could help you."

"But *where* would I find *them*?"

"You'd have to go out to sea . . . yes, out to sea."

"Which way is that?" asked Tom.

"Downstream!" said the otter, pointing, "Downstream!"

"Thank you, Mr Otter! Come on, Toby," called Tom, "that's for us! DOWNSTREAM!"

ISBN 0 00 123502 8
Copyright © 1978 Ariadne Films Ltd.
A Peter Shaw Production
Based on Charles Kingsley's classic story
Illustrations and text Copyright © 1978 William Collins Sons & Co. Ltd
Lyrics from the song "Try a Little Harder"
Copyright © 1978 Babies Music Publishing Ltd.
Printed and made in Great Britain

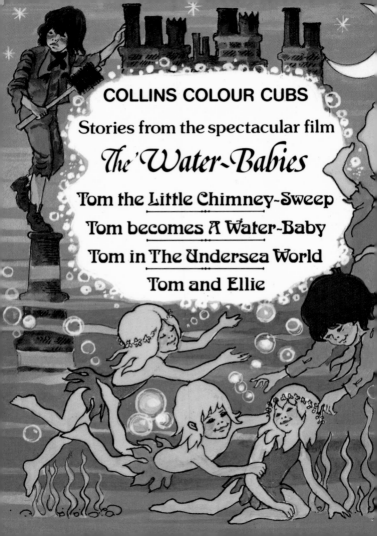

COLLINS COLOUR CUBS

Stories from the spectacular film

The Water-Babies

Tom the Little Chimney-Sweep

Tom becomes A Water-Baby

Tom in The Undersea World

Tom and Ellie

Author Biography

Andi Clevely has been a working gardener for nearly thirty years. He began his career in Leeds City Council central nurseries and since then has worked in many gardens around the country, including Windsor Great Park. He is now responsible for a country estate and large garden in Stratford-on-Avon where he lives with his family. Andi has written a number of gardening books and is a regular columnist for *Homes & Gardens* magazine.

Acknowledgements

The publishers would like to thank Secrets Garden Centre, Godalming, Surrey and Mrs Diana Hucker, Dulwich, London for their assistance with the photography. All photographs © BBC.

Published by BBC Books,
an imprint of BBC Worldwide Publishing.
BBC Worldwide Limited, Woodlands,
80 Wood Lane, London W12 0TT

First published 1997
© BBC Worldwide Limited 1997
The moral right of the author has been asserted

ISBN 0 563 38373 9

Photographs by Jo Whitworth

Artwork by Pond and Giles

Set in Futura

Printed and bound in Belgium by Proost NV
Colour separations by Radstock Reproductions Limited, Midsomer Norton, Avon
Cover printed in Belgium by Proost NV

BBC Books

Photographs by Jo Whitworth

Andi Clevely

HOUSE
PLANTS

POCKET PLANTS

BBC Gardeners' World

KU-042-088

BBC
Gardeners' World

POCKET PLANTS

HOUSE PLANTS

An essential guide to the best plants for your home

Symbols

Easy to grow

An undemanding or very robust plant, tolerating neglect or suitable for inexperienced growers.

Decorative value
Although any house plant may have other appealing qualities, each profile is identified by its most outstanding feature(s).

Flowers

Foliage

Fruits

Best position

Full sun: Likely to do well on a south-facing window-sill exposed to all but the hottest unfiltered sunshine.

Good light: Protect from direct sunshine most or all of the time, but expose to good light; ideal for east- or west-facing windows.

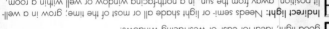
Indirect light: Needs semi- or light shade all or most of the time; grow in a well-lit position, away from the sun, in a north-facing window or well within a room.

Temperature
Although not absolutely critical, any plant will normally grow best at one of the following regimes.

Warm: Prefers fairly high temperatures of 16–20°C (61–68°F) or more.

Fairly warm: Thrives at an average of 10–16°C (50–61°F), although a little more or less does no harm.

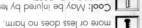
Cool: May be injured by temperatures much above the preferred range of 4–10°C (40–50°F).

Temperature Guide

Cool conditions

Arum Lily	80
Bead Plant	49
Calla Lily	80
Cineraria	69
Common Ivy	35
English Ivy	35
Indian Azalea	61
Italian Bellflower	14
Spider Plant	16
Star of Bethlehem	14

Fairly warm conditions

African Hemp	73
Aloe	8
Aluminium Plant	57
Asparagus Fern	9
Bromeliads	13
Calamondin Orange	18
Cape Grape	62
Cape Primrose	76
Cast Iron Plant	10
Century Plant	7
Christmas Cactus	66
Crassula	19
Devil's Backbone	44
Echeveria	26
Flame Nettle	72
Florists' Chrysanthemums	23
Florists' Cyclamen	20
Flowering Begonia	11

Grape Ivy	17, 62
Indian Crocus	59
Ivy Tree	30, 65
Japanese Aralia	31
Jerusalem Cherry	71
Palms	51
Piggyback Plant	77
Pink Jasmine	41
Prickly Pear	50
Regal Pelargonium	53
Ribbon Fern	60
Rose Mallow	36
Rose of China	36
Scented-leafed Geranium	52
Smilax	9
Spiderwort	78
Spineless Yucca	79
Stonecrop	68
String of Hearts	15
Swedish Ivy	58
Sweetheart Vine	15
Sword Fern	48
Table Fern	60
Umbrella Plant	22
Umbrella Tree	65
Velvet Plant	34
Wax Flower	38
Weeping Fig	32
Window-sill Orchid	59
Winter Cherry	71
Zonal Geranium	54

Warm conditions

African Violet	63
Amaryllis	37
Busy Lizzie	40
Crown of Thorns	27
Cymbidium	21
Devil's Ivy	67
Dragon Tree	25
Dumb Cane	24
Flaming Katy	43
German Violet	29
Gloxinia	70
Madagascar Jasmine	75
Maidenhair Fern	6
Mosaic Plant	3
Mother-in-law's Tongue	64
Painted Leaf Begonia	12
Peace Lily	74
Peperomia	55
Persian Violet	29
Philodendron	56
Poinsettia	28
Polka Dot Plant	39
Prayer Plant	46
Shrimp Plant	42
Shrub Verbena	45
Swiss-cheese Plant	47
Wax Flower	75
White Sails	74
Yellow Sage	45

Bold denotes easy to grow

INTRODUCTION

House plants have universal appeal, and there is a bewildering range of species. Evergreen foliage plants are very popular and offer colour all the year round. Flowering plants are the highlights. There are easy indestructible plants that tolerate neglect and thrive in less than ideal conditions, whereas some exotic or delicate species have precise likes and dislikes.

Situations for plants

The secret of success lies in finding the best position for any species.

Light: Aspect is very important, every plant needing some degree of light for good health. Grow those requiring full sun on or close to a south-facing window-sill or in a sunny porch; a few species may need light shade from hot midday sunshine. East- and west-facing windows offer very good light with some sun at various times of the day, while north-facing window-sills give bright sunless light or semi-shade. Distance away from a window decreases available light, and plants can be moved within a room according to their need for sun or shade.

Temperature: Temperature ranges suggested in this book are those ideal for healthy growth. Most plants will tolerate cooler or warmer periods without suffering, provided there is not too much fluctuation at critical times, such as early spring or late autumn and winter, when growth is either reviving or dying down. Remember some species need cooler or warmer conditions at certain times of year when they are resting or forming new buds.

Protect sensitive plants from frost by moving them inside curtains on cold nights. Ventilate where appropriate.

Repotting

Generally the choice of container is a matter for personal preference, although plastic pots help conserve moisture in the compost, and some plants with weak roots grow best in shallow pans or half-pots. Choose a size that just fits the rootball comfortably.

A standard soil-less or soil-based multi-purpose or house-plant compost suits most plants; any plant's preference for a particular kind is mentioned in its entry. Always use compost bought the same season as it is needed, and bring it inside to adjust to room or greenhouse temperature before potting.

Most house plants are repotted annually at the start of the growing season, either into the same size pot or one slightly larger – too great a difference may cause roots to rot in the larger volume of moist compost.

- Clean the new pot thoroughly if it has been used before. Cover the drainage hole in clay pots with pieces of broken pot. Where good drainage is essential, spread a layer of gravel or small stones in the bottom of the pot. Then fill with compost to the depth of the old pot.

- Water the plant and allow to drain for a few hours. Knock it out by inverting the pot, holding the contents with the fingers of one hand and tapping the rim of the pot on the edge of a table. Keep the soilball intact.

- Place the old pot inside the new one, fill around the sides with compost and firm or tap into place. Gently twist out the old pot to leave a hole the same size as the rootball. Set this in the hole, firm lightly or tap the new pot on the table to settle the contents, and water.

- When repotting into the same size pot, first carefully tease out the old crocks and some of the matted roots from the outside of the rootball, before replacing it in the pot. Trickle fresh compost around the edges, working it down with a pencil or dibber if necessary.

- With very large plants that are difficult to repot, simply scrape off the top 5cm (2in) of compost with a plant label or small trowel, taking care not to damage surface roots. Then refill with fresh compost and water.

Care

Watering: The commonest cause of failure with house plants is over- or under-watering. How much water to give, and when, varies widely according to the species and where it is grown. A particular plant will need more if kept in a warm room, a small pot or when actively growing, than it might in a cooler, shadier position or when growth is slowing down. The right quantity and frequency are both important. In some cases the water should be warm or allowed to reach room temperature, and a few species prefer soft water or rainwater. Plants are more likely to recover from under-watering than being waterlogged.

The amount of water in the air is also important, especially with thin-leafed or tropical species which need high humidity to keep their foliage in good condition: misting with a fine spray and standing pots on a bed of pebbles partly covered with water both help to provide a humid atmosphere, especially in warm dry rooms like living rooms.

Feeding: There is enough fertilizer in fresh potting compost to sustain plants for about six weeks, after which regular feeding usually becomes necessary for the rest of the active growing season. Use a liquid or soluble house-plant or balanced general purpose fertilizer. Some plants, especially during flowering, need extra potassium, supplied by a high-potash feed such as tomato fertilizer. Slow-release fertilizers in stick or pellet form will often last for the whole season. Any plant's specific preference is mentioned in its entry.

Rest: Most house plants alternate active growth with a quiet resting period, when they should be kept cooler and often drier than at other times. Some plants start to die down and become dormant at this time, while the growth of evergreens slows down as light levels and day lengths decrease. These resting periods are important for a plant's health and affect its performance the following season.

Training and pruning: Weak or long-stemmed plants, and any with heavy flower heads can be tied loosely to thin canes to keep them tidy. Climbers need sturdier support like a wire hoop, wooden trellis or moss-sticks, and stems should be trained and tied to these at regular intervals unless the plant is self-supporting.

Some climbers can be trained as bushy plants if their growing tips are pinched out regularly; most plants need this simple attention now and then during active growth to encourage branching. Pruning is a more comprehensive annual event, often at repotting time: cut off surplus growth with secateurs to restore the original size and shape.

Pests and diseases: All plants should be inspected regularly for the first signs of trouble. Aim to prevent disorders by encouraging strong healthy growth, and use a standard insecticide or fungicide promptly if problems occur. Isolate any ailing plant until it has fully recovered.

Adiantum Maidenhair Fern

ADIANTUM RADDIANUM

Most of these popular graceful ferns originate in semitropical rainforests where they enjoy warmth and moisture at all times. They are elegant plants with delicate thread-like stems that arch charmingly, especially when trailing from the sides of a hanging basket.

Positioning:	Warm window-sill or room with good humidity; away from sunlight, draughts. Better in a shady conservatory than a living room.
Season:	Foliage all year.
Height:	30–75cm (12–30in).
Spread:	60–90cm (24–30in).
Care:	Soak regularly to keep roots moist, ideally with tepid soft water. Stand pots on pebbles in dishes of water. Apply fertilizer fortnightly from spring to late summer. Repot rootbound plants in spring in soil-less compost; do not bury crowns. Cut dry shrivelled fronds to soil level.
Propagation:	Divide plants in spring.
Recommended:	*A. formosum*; *A. raddianum*, syn *A. cuneatum* (vigorous), basic species and 'Gympie Gold', 'Fritz Luthie', 'Fragrantissimum'; *A. tenerum*.
Useful tip:	*A. capillus-veneris* (Common Maidenhair Fern) is an attractive plant for cool rooms.

Positioning: Warm bright window-sill.

Season: Foliage all year.

Height: 15–90cm (6in–3ft).

Spread: 15cm–1.2m (6in–4ft).

Care: Water freely from spring to autumn as necessary, every 1–2 months in winter or whenever compost dries out. Apply fertilizer fortnightly between mid-spring and early autumn. If essential, repot in early spring in a slightly larger pot; use a soil-based compost covered with grit or coarse sand for drainage. Remove dead shrivelled leaves.

Propagation: Pot up offsets or runners.

Recommended: A. victoriae-reginae (the smallest species); A. americana and coloured forms 'Marginata', 'Variegata', 'Mediopicta' (some of the largest); also A. celsii; A. stricta; A. filifera.

Useful tip: Stand outdoors in a sunny sheltered spot in a dry summer.

AGAVE POTATORUM

These dominating succulents vary from compact miniatures to giant tub-plants. In temperate climates they increase in size slowly and seldom flower, which is fortunate because the main rosette then sets seed and dies.

Aloe Aloe

ALOE VARIEGATA

Sunny window-sill or conservatory in summer; cool well-lit place like a bedroom window in winter.

Season: Foliage all year; flowers at various seasons.

Height: 10–30cm (4–12in)

Spread: 15–30cm (6–12in)

Care: Undemanding. Water from below whenever the compost is quite dry during growth; very sparingly in winter. Avoid over-watering and wetting the foliage. Apply fertilizer fortnightly from mid-spring to early autumn. Repot every 3–4 years in spring in a soil-based compost; cover the surface with grit or coarse sand for good drainage.

Propagation: Pot up offsets.

Recommended: A. aristata (dense bristly rosettes); A. vera; A. variegata; A. humilis; A. mitriformis.

Useful tip: Cool winter conditions (about 5°C/41°F) stimulate flower buds to form.

Aloes are sometimes confused with Agaves, but are quite distinct plants, with rosettes that flower more freely and do not die afterwards. Many are small, grow very slowly and tolerate a lot of neglect. Find sunny places for them in summer for the best leaf and flower colours.

Asparagus   Asparagus Fern, Smilax

Positioning: Bright or semi-shaded positions; keep out of direct sunlight. Trail on stands or in hanging baskets.

Season: Foliage all year.

Height: Up to 3m (10ft).

Spread: 60–90cm (2–3ft).

Care: Water regularly from spring to autumn; more sparingly in winter. Occasional dryness or over-watering is tolerated. Apply fertilizer every 10–14 days in summer; never in winter if kept cool, every month in a warm room. Repot young plant in soil-based compost every spring, older ones every 2–3 years. Let long-stemmed forms trail, or train them on canes or a moss-stick.

Propagation: Divide at any time.

Recommended: A. setaceus, syn. A. plumosus; A. p. 'Nanus' (compact); A. densiflorus Sprengeri Group; also A. asparagoides.

Useful tip: Avoid very high temperatures which may cause leaf drop.

ASPARAGUS PLUMOSUS

These are evergreen perennials, not true ferns, with 'leaves' (really modified branches) like needles. They are easier to grow than ferns, and tolerate some neglect. As a bonus, tiny white flowers appear in early summer, followed sometimes by red berries.

Aspidistra Cast Iron Plant

ASPIDISTRA ELATIOR 'VARIEGATA'

This is an old favourite, familiar as one of the few house plants to thrive in gloomy positions where the sun never reaches. Plants take deep shade, draughts, air pollution and drought in their stride; they are threatened only by over-watering and frequent repotting.

Positioning: Green forms in full shade, variegated kinds in semi-shade. Display within a room rather than on a window-sill. Keep at 7–10°C (45–50°F) in winter.

Season: Foliage all year.

Height: 90cm (3ft).

Spread: 90cm (3ft).

Care: Water regularly from spring to autumn; let compost dry out between waterings. Give less in winter. Apply fertilizer monthly in spring and summer. Repot into slightly larger pots in mid-spring every 4–5 years. Do not feed during the following season. Sponge or shower dusty leaves. Never stand pots in stagnant water.

Propagation: Divide mature specimens in spring.

Recommended: *A. elatior*, basic dark green species and the cream-striped form 'Variegata'.

Useful tip: Mature plants have flowers at the base of their stems in winter or early spring.

Begonia (flowering) Flowering Begonia

Positioning: Well-lit, away from direct sunlight except in winter. Avoid temperatures above 21°C (70°F).

Season: Flowers in summer, winter or all year round.

Height: 30–45cm (12–18in), cane-stemmed types up to 1.8m (6ft).

Spread: 45cm (18in).

Care: Water regularly from spring to autumn; let the surface dry out between waterings. Water less often in winter. Stand pots on pebbles in saucers of water. Apply fertilizer every 10–14 days during flowering. Repot in spring in soil-less compost. Pinch stems a few times; support later growth with thin canes. Deadhead regularly.

Propagation: Grow leaf or soft cuttings from lower side-shoots at any time.

Recommended: *B. coccinea* (tall); *B. × corallina*, *B. × 'Lucerna Amazon'* (tall); *B. semperflorens*; *B. scharffii*; *B. sutherlandii*.

Useful tip: Grow tall varieties in clay pots for stability.

WINTER-FLOWERING HYBRID

Evergreen flowering begonias tend to have smaller flowers, but often compensate with their attractive foliage, and are exotic and satisfying all-round plants. Wax Begonias (*B. semperflorens*) are the easiest of these, often grown for annual bedding outdoors.

11

Begonia (foliage types) Painted Leaf Begonia

REX CULTIVAR

There are dozens of varieties, all with remarkable leaf colours, patterns and textures. Most of them make dense mounds of beautiful foliage although some species trail or climb. They are fibrous-rooted plants which often produce small pink or white flowers in clusters: these may be pinched off or left as a bonus.

Positioning: Well-lit, away from direct sunshine except in winter; protect from draughts.

Season: Foliage all year.

Height: 23–30cm (9–12in).

Spread: 30–45cm (12–18in).

Care: Water regularly in spring and summer; let the surface dry out between waterings. Water sparingly in winter. Avoid over-watering. Stand pots on pebbles in saucers of water. Never spray the leaves. Apply high-potash fertilizer fortnightly in spring, summer. Repot in spring, in soil-less compost. Turn pots occasionally for even growth.

Propagation: Divide large plants at repotting time.

Recommended: B. 'Cleopatra'; B. masoniana; B. rex hybrids, like 'Black Knight' and 'President Carnot'; B. 'Tiger'.

Useful tip: Too much shade causes plants to develop long limp stems which are often prone to mildew.

Bromeliaceae Bromeliads

Positioning:	Good light, shaded from direct sunshine.
Season:	Foliage and flowers all year.
Height:	30–60cm (1–2ft).
Spread:	Up to 45cm (18in).
Care:	Keep central rosettes of leaves filled with rainwater; replace this with clean water every 2 months. Mist leaves regularly in summer. Plants need evenly moist compost. Add one or two drops of liquid fertilizer now and then when watering or misting leaves. Non-flowering plants rarely need repotting.
Propagation:	Pot up offsets.
Recommended:	*Aechmea fasciata, A. f. 'Foster's Favorite'; Ananas comosus* var. *variegatus; Billbergia nutans; Guzmania lingulata; Neoregelia carolinae, N. c.* var. *tricolor; Tillandsia cyanea; Vriesia splendens.*
Useful tip:	Grow separately in small pots or in compost-filled holes bored into an old branch.

ANANAS COMOSUS VAR. AUREOVARIEGATUS

Bromeliads are very easy to grow as brightly coloured evergreen foliage plants, thriving at only 10°C (50°F). Most form rosettes of leaves that hold a reservoir of water. All the plants in this huge group have very small root systems and a tendency to die after flowering, leaving young offsets to continue growing – these can be potted up in soil-less compost.

Campanula isophylla Italian Bellflower, Star of Bethlehem

CAMPANULA ISOPHYLLA

This old-fashioned house plant is a favourite, very easy to grow, and rewarding when its densely branching stems are smothered in masses of star-shaped blooms 4cm (1½in) across. It is sensitive to frost, but should be grown as cool as possible to prolong the spectacular display. A natural trailer, ideal for a hanging basket.

Positioning: Well-lit or slightly shaded window, shielded from bright summer sunshine.

Season: Flowers all summer and early autumn.

Height: 30cm (12in) (also trailing).

Spread: Up to 45cm (18in).

Care: Keep evenly moist during growth, just damp at other times: reduce watering in mid-autumn. In summer check plants in warm positions twice daily. Mist plants occasionally. Apply fertilizer weekly from spring to early autumn. Repot in spring in rich soil-based compost, water once and keep below 15°C (60°F). Deadhead regularly. Trim growth to 5cm (2in) in mid-autumn. Keep cool in winter.

Propagation: Divide mature plants at repotting time.

Recommended: Basic species; 'Alba', 'Flore Pleno', 'Mayi'; C. 'Balchiniana'.

Useful tip: Keep cool to prolong flowering or stand outdoors in light shade in summer.

Positioning: Well-lit window, in full sun or light shade; in a hanging pot or trailing from a shelf. Keep in full sun at about 10°C (50°F) in winter ideally in an unheated greenhouse or conservatory.

Season: Foliage all year.

Size: Trails to 90cm (3ft).

Care: Water sparingly; reduce amounts in autumn, give very little in winter. Apply cactus fertilizer every fortnight in spring and summer. Repot in spring, only if rootbound, in half-pots; use cactus compost or a soil-based compost with added grit. Cut back stems in spring to induce branching.

Propagation: Grow stem cuttings at any time.

Recommended: C. linearis ssp. woodii, syn. C. woodii;
C. africana,
C. barkleyi (climbers or trailers);
C. sandersonii.

Useful tip: Plants tolerate a dry atmosphere and may be kept in a living room all year.

CEROPEGIA WOODII

Ceropegias are succulents and come in many shapes and forms. The unusual group with thread-like trailing stems, sparse round or heart-shaped leaves (often with pretty markings) and strange tubular or lantern-shaped flowers is especially popular.

Chlorophytum comosum

CHLOROPHYTUM COMOSUM 'VARIEGATUM'

Popular and virtually indestructible, the spider plant is usually seen in one of its variegated forms. It thrives almost anywhere, on a cool window-sill or in dry central heating, and quickly develops into a handsome bush with cascades of young plantlets on long arching stems. (syn. *C. sternbergianum*.)

Positioning: Well-lit window-sill, in full sun or light shade, where the stems can trail freely.

Season: Foliage all year; small white flowers in summer.

Height: Up to 45cm (18in).

Spread: Much greater than height if flower stems are retained.

Care: Water freely from spring to autumn, sparingly in winter. Do not allow to dry out. Mist occasionally. Feed with fertilizer every 10–14 days, spring to autumn. Repot in soil-less compost in spring or when rootbound. Train flower stems on a wire hoop or let them trail and form aerial plantlets.

Propagation: Root plantlets singly in small pots in spring.

Recommended: All-green species; also 'Variegatum' and 'Vittatum'.

Useful tip: Brown leaf tips are caused by draughts, under-watering or irregular feeding. Cut them off at an angle to create a new tip.

Cissus Grape Ivy

Positioning: Well-lit or semi-shaded, away from direct sunshine. Give vigorous forms plenty of space.

Season: Foliage all year.

Height: 3m (10ft) or more.

Spread: 45cm (18in).

Care: Water regularly from spring to autumn, sparingly in winter unless kept in warmth (above 8°C/46°F). Mist leaves monthly. Apply fertilizer weekly from the appearance of new shoots until late summer. Repot in spring if necessary, in soil-based compost. Pinch out stem tips and train long stems on canes, moss-sticks or trellis.

Propagation: Grow tip cuttings in late summer.

Recommended: C. antarctica (vigorous), 'Minima' (more compact); C. discolor; C. striata; C. rhombifolia, syn. Rhoicissus rhomboidea.

Useful tip: If kept warm in winter, check regularly for red spider mites.

CISSUS ANTARCTICA

These evergreen vines are tough and tolerant, great favourites for semi-shaded corners of living rooms. They survive with little attention, but look much more lush and healthy if fed and misted regularly. Many *Rhoicissus* species are now included under *Cissus*.

× *CITROFORTUNELLA MICROCARPA*

This is the easiest citrus fruit to grow as a house plant, and makes a handsome evergreen shrub, long-lived and capable of fruiting while still young. Very often the white fragrant flowers appear all year with the small bitter fruits, which make an excellent marmalade. (syn. *Citrus mitis*.)

Positioning: Sunniest window-sill or bright conservatory.

Season: Flowers and fruits all year.

Height: Up to 1.2m (4ft).

Spread: 90cm (3ft).

Care: Water freely all year but avoid over-watering: keep cool and just moist in winter. Mist leaves now and then except during flowering. Apply fertilizer weekly from 6 weeks after repotting to late summer. Repot in spring in well-drained soil-based compost; avoid damage to the roots. Replace top 5cm (2in) of compost with fresh for larger plants. Thin congested shoots in spring and shorten longer ones.

Propagation: Grow tip cuttings in spring.

Recommended: Basic species and 'Tiger', 'Variegata'; also *Citrus limon*, *C. l.* 'Variegata'; *C.* × *sinensis* 'Meyer' (compact).

Useful tip: Inspect regularly for scale insects and treat them as soon as seen.

Crassula Crassula

Positioning: Bright sunny window-sill or conservatory; protect white- and grey-leafed kinds from midday sunshine.

Season: Foliage all year.

Height: 60cm–1.2m (2–4ft) or more.

Spread: Up to 1.2m (4ft).

Care: Water sparingly at all times. Withhold water in winter below 7°C (45°F). Spray foliage if it is dusty, otherwise keep in a dry atmosphere. Apply half-strength fertilizer monthly from spring to early autumn. Repot in spring in soil-based compost with added grit then water carefully for a few weeks. Ventilate in summer. Keep cool in winter (6–10°C/43–50°F).

Propagation: Grow tip or leaf cuttings at any time.

Recommended: C. arborescens; C. ovata, syns. C. argentea and C. portulacea, including 'Basutoland', 'Hummel's Sunset'.

Useful tip: A cool period in winter often stimulates flowering.

CRASSULA OVATA

Some crassulas grow as dainty trailers while others, such as the immensely popular jade plant or money tree (*C. ovata*) eventually make large branching shrubs or even small trees. Most are succulents, all are easily grown in normal room conditions.

Cyclamen persicum Florists' Cyclamen

CYCLAMEN HYBRID

These lovely plants can be temperamental if kept too warm or allowed to dry out. They are often bought and then discarded after flowering, but with a little care they may be kept for many years and eventually make enormous plants. Keep bought ones in a cool place for a few days before introducing to a warm room.

Positioning: Bright, away from direct sunshine; lightly shaded window-sill. Avoid heaters and radiators.

Season: Flowers autumn to early spring.

Height: 15–30cm (6–12in).

Spread: 15–45cm (6–18in).

Care: Water with tepid rainwater, liberally when flowering otherwise moderately. Always immerse pots. Stand on pebbles in saucers of water; mist foliage regularly when not flowering. Apply fertilizer fortnightly during growth and flowering. Repot in late summer or early autumn in soil-based compost; bury corms to half their depth.

Propagation: Surface-sow seeds in late winter or late summer.

Recommended: 'Benary's Special', 'Decora', 'Olympia', 'Rex', Scentsation', 'Triumph'; miniature 'Puppet', 'Wellensiek Mini-mix'.

Useful tip: Older plants do not need repotting every year.

Cymbidium Cymbidium

Positioning: Good light, shaded from hot sunshine; warm room with temperatures about 5°C (10°F) lower at night.

Season: Flowers winter, spring or summer according to variety.

Height: 23–90cm (9–36in).

Spread: Up to 45cm (18in).

Care: Water with room-temperature rainwater, while growing, sparingly at other times. Keep barely moist while dormant. Mist leaves now and then or stand pots on pebbles in saucers of water. Apply orchid fertilizer fortnightly during growth. Repot in orchid compost every 2–3 years at the start of growing season.

Propagation: Divide at repotting time.

Recommended: Babylon 'Castle Hill', Pink Ice 'Foxgrove', Showgirl, Swallow 'Exbury'; C. lowianum; C. eburneum.

Useful tip: Provide artificial light in winter; plants always need 10–15 hours.

PINK ICE 'FOXGROVE'

Many orchids are easy to grow in the home. Cymbidium varieties are some of the most popular; they remain healthy under ordinary room conditions and regularly produce magnificent spikes of gorgeous waxy blooms, often with a bizarrely marked lip.

Cyperus Umbrella Plant

CYPERUS DIFFUSUS

The symmetrical radiating shape of these fine structural plants complements most decors. As they are semi-aquatic species, it is difficult to over-water them and most problems occur in dry atmospheres. Dwarf forms show to advantage in bottle gardens or tanks of ornamental pebbles.

Positioning: Good light, away from strong sunshine; light shade, cool conditions tolerated. Ideal for conservatories, bottle gardens.

Season: Foliage all year.

Height: 30cm–1.8m (1–6ft).

Spread: 45–90cm (18–36in).

Care: Keep evenly moist; stand *C. papyrus*, *C. involucratus* in containers of water. Mist leaves regularly with tepid water. Apply fertilizer weekly from spring to autumn. Repot in spring in soil-based compost with added charcoal. Cut out yellowing stems to encourage growth.

Propagation: Divide plants at repotting time.

Recommended: *C. albostriatus*, syn. *C. diffusus*, and 'Variegatus'; *C. alternifolius*, syn. *C. involucratus*, best forms *gracilis* and 'Nanus' (both dwarf); *C. papyrus*.

Useful tip: A dry atmosphere encourages greenfly, can also cause leaf tips to turn brown.

Positioning: Bright light, shaded from direct midday sun; ideal on a window-sill that receives early morning or evening sunshine.

Season: Normally autumn; bought plants available in flower all year.

Height: 30–45cm (12–18in).

Spread: 30–45cm (12–18in).

Care: Keep evenly moist. Feed Charms with fertilizer weekly until buds show colour. Pot on growing plants whenever they are rootbound, in soil-based compost; end in 15–20cm (6–8in) pots. Pinch out growing tips once or twice (not needed for Charms). Deadhead.

Propagation: Grow tip cuttings between early winter and early spring.

Recommended: Charms: 'Redbreast', 'Golden Chalice', 'Ring Dove'. Marguerites (Argyranthemum frutescens): 'Jamaica Primrose', 'Petite Pink', 'Qinta White', 'Rollason's Red'.

Useful tip: Watch out for aphids and red spider mites.

CHRYSANTHEMUM HYBRID

Most florists' chrysanthemums are bought in bud or flower, and discarded afterwards because they are grown under special conditions to keep them compact. They are popular house plants, however, and Charm varieties can survive from one year to another. Marguerites are closely related, and will flower all summer and autumn. (syn. Chrysanthemum hybrids.)

Dieffenbachia Dumb Cane

DIEFFENBACHIA PICTA

These striking evergreen perennials, related to arum lilies, have handsome variegated or brightly mottled leaves that can reach 75cm (30in) long. They are tropical plants, adapted to high humidity and dappled sunlight, and their beauty may be short-lived in a dry atmosphere or if they are exposed to cold draughts.

Positioning: Well-lit room or gently shaded window-sill; away from bright sunshine, draughts.

Season: Foliage all year.

Height: 1.2m (4ft).

Spread: 90cm (3ft).

Care: Water with tepid rainwater, regularly from spring to autumn, sparingly in winter; let surface dry between waterings but avoid plants drying out. Apply fertilizer fortnightly from spring to late summer. Mist leaves frequently; stand pots on pebbles in saucers of water. Repot in spring in soil-less compost and cut old leggy plants back to about 15cm (6in).

Propagation: Grow tip cuttings in spring.

Recommended: D. maculata, syn. D. picta, D. m. 'Camilla', 'Jenmannii', 'Tropic White'; D. seguine, D. s. 'Amoena', 'Tropic Snow'.

Useful tip: The plant sap irritates mucous membranes, so wash hands after taking cuttings.

Dracaena Dragon Tree

Positioning: Very good light for bright colours; shield plants from midday sunshine, cold draughts. Keep slightly cooler in winter (minimum 10°C/50°F).

Season: Foliage all year.

Height: Up to 3m (10ft) or more.

Spread: 90cm–1.2m (3–4ft).

Care: Water freely from late spring to early autumn, otherwise more sparingly. Compost must always be moist but not waterlogged. Mist leaves regularly while growing. Apply fertilizer fortnightly from spring to late summer. Repot in spring, in well-drained soil-based compost, young plants annually, older ones every 2–3 years.

Propagation: Grow tip cuttings in spring.

Recommended: *D. deremensis* 'Warneckii', 'Yellow Stripe'; *D. marginata*, *D. m.* 'Colorama'; *D. fragrans*, *D. f.* 'Massangeana'.

Useful tip: Cuttings of variegated forms are green before colours appear.

DRACAENA MARGINATA 'TRICOLOR'

Most Dracaena varieties eventually grow into tall graceful plants with bare stems crowned by a rosette of arching leaves. They are bold plants for strategic places such as a hallway or large living room, where a well-grown specimen can be dramatic and eye-catching.

Echeveria Echeveria

ECHEVERIA CILIATA

These popular and easy-going succulents thrive in dry sunny conditions which might be lethal to softer plants. Although grown for their rosettes of thick leaves, often covered in attractive bloom, many species also produce tall spikes of bright red, yellow or orange flowers.

Positioning: Full sun; preferably a fairly dry atmosphere. Keep cool and barely moist in winter.

Season: Foliage all year.

Height: Up to 60cm (2ft) but usually less.

Spread: 15–30cm (6–12in).

Care: Wait for compost to dry out then soak thoroughly; in winter water every 1–2 months. Wetting foliage too often damages the wax layer. Feed with half-strength cactus fertilizer monthly from spring to late summer. Repot in spring in a gritty cactus compost, young plants annually, older ones every 2–3 years.

Propagation: Pot up tops of bare stems, basal offsets or complete leaves at any time.

Recommended: E. agavoides; E. elegans; E. setosa; E. derenbergii; E. harmsii, syn. Oliveranthus elegans.

Useful tip: Cutting the tops from bare-stemmed plants will cause side-shoots to develop lower down.

Euphorbia milii Crown of Thorns

Positioning:	Warm window-sill; full sunshine.
Season:	Flowers early spring to mid-summer, or longer.
Height:	Up to 90cm (3ft).
Spread:	60cm (2ft).
Care:	Keep moderately moist from spring to autumn, almost dry in winter; let the surface dry out between waterings. Avoid poor drainage. Apply cactus fertilizer fortnightly, spring to late summer. Repot in spring in sandy or gritty soil-based compost, young plants every 1–2 years, older ones after 3–4 years. Pinch out shoot tips now and then. Rest in a dry place (minimum temperature 13°C/55°F) in winter.
Propagation:	Grow tip cuttings in spring or summer.
Recommended:	Basic species, and 'Koenigers Aalbäumle' (dwarf) and var. splendens; E. fulgens; E. meloformis (dwarf); E. submammilaris (dwarf) and form 'Variegata'.
Useful tip:	Leaves may drop if plants are moved to a different aspect.

EUPHORBIA MILII

Perhaps the best known of the succulent Euphorbias, this is a robust and undemanding plant that can tolerate considerable neglect and still produce its bright immaculate flowers, usually in spring but often all year round if well tended. Handle with respect and keep well away from children: stems are very thorny and the sap is poisonous.

Euphorbia pulcherrima Poinsettia

EUPHORBIA PULCHERRIMA 'MENORCA'

This tall Central American perennial has become one of the most popular seasonal pot plants for winter colour. It is easy to keep from one year to the next but, unless given special day-length treatment, will tend to produce its red, pink-or white blooms in spring on taller plants than before.

Positioning: Well-lit; away from full sunshine, draughts.

Season: Flowers winter and spring.

Height: Up to 90cm (3ft).

Spread: 45–60cm (18–24in).

Care: Soak thoroughly when growing and flowering; let the surface dry between waterings. Keep almost dry from leaf-fall to early summer. Mist foliage occasionally. Apply fertilizer weekly from early summer until early winter. Repot in late spring or early summer and cut plants back by half. Thin new shoots to leave 4–5 stems. Discard plants after flowering or reduce watering and leave dormant for a few weeks before repotting.

Propagation: Grow tip cuttings in spring or summer.

Recommended: All varieties including 'Annette Hegg', 'Ruth Ecke', 'Rosea', 'Ecke's White'.

Useful tip: For early winter flowers keep in a dark cupboard for 14 hours daily for 8 weeks, from early autumn.

Exacum affine German Violet, Persian Violet

Positioning: Well-lit corner, away from strong sunlight, draughts.

Season: Flowers mid-summer to late autumn.

Height: Up to 30cm (12in).

Spread: 23–30cm (9–12in).

Care: Keep evenly moist during growth, ideally with rainwater. Mist leaves now and then. Apply fertilizer fortnightly while growing and flowering. Pinch out growing tips of young plants. Give plenty of fresh air until buds form. Deadhead but let last flowers set seeds. Discard plants after flowering.

Propagation: Surface-sow seeds in late winter under glass.

Recommended: Seed strains include 'Rosendal Blue', 'Rosendal Mixed' and var. atrocaeruleum, 'Midget', 'White Midget' (both dwarf), 'Elfin' (compact).

Useful tip: Plants flower when about 6 months old; a batch sown in late summer will produce larger plants that will flower a little earlier the following year.

EXACUM AFFINE

These cheerful plants are biennial or short-lived perennials, difficult to keep from one year to the next and so are usually grown as annuals. They set plenty of seeds, which quickly germinate and grow into bushy plants that are covered in gold-centred blooms, up to 2.5cm (1in) across and very fragrant.

× *FATSHEDERA LIZEI*

This fast-growing evergreen climber, produced by crossing the palm-leafed *Fatsia japonica* with ivy, is easily pleased and soon reaches a great height if trained on supports. It is equally happy pinched out to make a superb bush of rich green or prettily variegated glossy leaves.

Positioning: Light shade at all times; fairly bright light in winter, especially in warm rooms. Place green forms in shadier corners.

Season: Foliage all year.

Height: 1.8m (6ft) or more.

Spread: 45–60cm (18–24in).

Care: Water regularly from spring to autumn, less freely in winter; make sure plants never dry out but avoid saturation. Mist leaves regularly. Apply fertilizer fortnightly spring to autumn. Repot in spring in rich soil-based compost. Train as climbers on canes or trellis, or pinch out growing tips now and then for bushy plants.

Propagation: Grow tip cuttings in late summer.

Recommended: Basic species, 'Pia' 'Annemieke', 'Aurea', 'Variegata'.

Useful tip: Group 3–4 young plants in one pot for mass impact: plants naturally tend to grow as slim single-stemmed climbers.

Fatsia japonica Japanese Aralia

Positioning:	Light shade; ideal in halls, unheated conservatories, other cool areas normally below 21°C (70°F).
Season:	Foliage all year.
Height:	1.2–1.5m (4–5ft).
Spread:	Up to 1.2m (4ft).
Care:	Water freely during active growth from spring to late summer, sparsly in winter and moderately at other times. Do not let compost dry out. Mist leaves regularly in spring, summer. Apply fertilizer weekly from spring to late summer. Repot in spring in soil-based compost and pinch out all growing tips. Nip out autumn flower buds.
Propagation:	Grow tip cuttings in summer.
Recommended:	Basic species, 'Albomarginata', 'Aurea', 'Variegata', 'Moseri'; also *Tetrapanax papyrifer*, syn. *Fatsia papyrifer*.
Useful tip:	Yellowing leaves usually indicate too much heat or over-watering.

FATSIA JAPONICA

Japanese aralia is the perfect, durable evergreen shrub for cool or shady rooms, tolerant enough to thrive in a wide range of situations and even withstand a little neglect. Its palm-shaped leaves can reach 38cm (15in) or more across, their glossy surfaces shining as though varnished.

Ficus benjamina Weeping Fig

FICUS BENJAMINA 'STARLIGHT'

This is one of the most attractive Ficus species, its fast growth and weeping tree-like habit making it a popular choice for the home. The arching branches and long pendent evergreen leaves give it a unique airy grace.

Positioning:	Best possible light; out of direct sunshine.
Season:	Foliage all year.
Height:	2m (6½ft) or more.
Spread:	Up to 1.2m (4ft).
Care:	Water with tepid water, freely from early spring to mid-autumn, sparingly in winter; let the surface dry out between waterings. Adjust amounts to suit the temperature. Mist leaves now and then with tepid water. Apply fertilizer every 10–14 days, spring to late summer. Repot in spring, small plants annually, older specimens every 2–3 years and top-dress large plants annually: replace the top 5cm (2in) of compost. Treat pruned cuts with charcoal.
Propagation:	Air-layer the ends of shoots in spring or summer.
Recommended:	Basic species, 'Golden King', 'Starlight'; also *F. elastica*, *F. e.* 'Robusta'; *F. lyrata*.
Useful tip:	Choose a permanent position with a fairly constant temperature.

Fittonia   Mosaic Plant

Positioning: Light shade, humidity; ideal for terrariums and bottle gardens. Keep above 15°C (60°F) in winter.

Season: Foliage all year.

Height: 10–15cm (4–6in).

Spread: 15cm (6in) or more.

Care: Keep moist with tepid rainwater from spring to early autumn, a little drier at other times. Stand pots on pebbles in saucers of water. Mist leaves every few days in spring and summer. Apply half-strength ericaceous fertilizer fortnightly from spring to late summer. Repot in spring in well-drained ericaceous compost in shallow pans.

Propagation: Separate rooted runners and pot up at any time.

Recommended: *F. albivenis* Argyneura Group, syn. *F. verschaffeltii* var. *argyneura*, 'Nana' (more compact); also *F. verschaffeltii* var. *pearcei*.

Useful tip: Growth is straggly, but untidy plants may be trimmed to shape at repotting time.

FITTONIA ALBIVENIS

Fittonia is popular for its daintily veined leaves and dense creeping habit. A well-grown potful looks stunning, but it is often easier to let it romp as colourful ground cover beneath taller plants in a heated conservatory.

Gynura Velvet Plant

GYNURA SARMENTOSA

Gynuras are rewarding and unusual climbing or trailing plants, popular for their easy culture and the remarkable velvety purple hairs that make the leaves gleam in bright light. The flowers, usually yellow and rather like withering dandelions, have an unpleasant smell at first and later turn into silvery balls.

Positioning: Brightest possible light; away from direct sunshine, draughts.

Season: Foliage all year.

Size: Trails to 90cm (3ft) or more; 30–45cm (12–18in) wide.

Care: Water freely from spring to mid-autumn, otherwise sparingly. Do not spray or wet leaves. Feed with half-strength high-potash fertilizer every 3–4 weeks, spring and summer. Repot in spring, young plants annually, older ones if necessary. Pinch out growing tips for bushy growth. Remove buds if the flowers' scent is offensive. Keep at a minimum 12°C (54°F) in winter; plants must not dry out to the point of wilting.

Propagation: Grow tip cuttings in spring or autumn.

Recommended: *G. aurantiaca*, *G. a.* 'Purple Passion', syn. 'Sarmentosa'; *G. procumbens* (more trailing habit).

Useful tip: Avoid overfeeding, which can spoil the rich leaf colouring.

Hedera helix   Common Ivy, English Ivy

Positioning: Green forms in shade, variegated in good light; shield from strong sunshine. Keep cool (maximum 15°C/60°F) in winter.
Season: Foliage all year.
Height: 30cm–1.8m (1–6ft).
Spread: 45cm (18in) or more.
Care: Water regularly from spring to autumn, sparingly in winter; always keep the compost evenly moist. Mist leaves regularly. Feed fortnightly with fertilizer in spring and summer. Repot in spring if rootbound (every 2–3 years) in soil-less compost in plastic pots. Tie stems in to canes, moss-sticks or trellis, or trail from hanging baskets, raised pots.
Propagation: Grow tip cuttings under glass at any time.
Recommended: 'Garland' (non-climbing), 'Glacier', 'Green Ripple' (bushy) 'Jubilee' (syn. 'Goldheart'), 'Parsley Crested', 'Sagittifolia'.
Useful tip: The aerial roots may cling to woodwork and wallpaper, so provide alternative support.

IVY HYBRID

These popular fast-growing evergreen climbers may also be trained as trailing plants and dense bushes. The variety of leaf shapes, colour combinations and markings is almost infinite. All types make reliable house plants that remain in good condition at temperatures as low as 3°C (37°F).

Hibiscus rosa-sinensis Rose of China, Rose Mallow

HIBISCUS ROSA-SINENSIS

These long-lived shrubs produce exotic papery blooms, each lasting only a few days but followed steadily by a succession of others from spring until autumn. Double forms are flamboyant but often untidy, and the single varieties are the most popular.

Positioning: Warm sunny window while growing; a slightly cooler position in winter (12–15°C/ 54–60°F). Avoid draughts.

Season: Flowers spring to autumn.

Height: Up to 2m (6½ft).

Spread: 90cm–1.2m (3–4ft).

Care: Keep evenly moist during growth; plunge pots in buckets of water if necessary. Spray foliage now and then. Water sparingly in winter but do not allow to dry out. Apply fertilizer fortnightly in spring and summer. Repot in spring in well-drained soil-based compost. Large plants may be top-dressed: replace the top 5cm (2in) of compost. Shorten stems by one-third in late winter. Deadhead.

Propagation: Grow tip cuttings under glass in spring or summer.

Recommended: Basic red, orange, yellow and white forms; 'Cooperi'; also *H. schizopetalus*.

Useful tip: Plants may be trained as standards.

Hippeastrum Amaryllis

Positioning: Warm sunny window during growth; in cool shade while resting.

Season: Flowers early winter to late spring.

Height: 60cm (2ft) or more.

Spread: 45–60cm (18–24in).

Care: Water sparingly at first, ideally with rainwater, increasing amount as leaves and flower stalks develop. Dry off after mid-summer. Feed with fertilizer fortnightly during growth. Repot every 2–3 years in well-drained soil-based compost. Leave bulb necks exposed. Water, keep in a warm place. Cut off flower stalks after flowering. Dry off bulbs in late summer and rest for 4–5 weeks.

Propagation: Pot up offsets.

Recommended: 'Apple Blossom', 'Best Seller', 'Bouquet', 'Fire Dance', 'Picotee', 'Red Lion', 'White Dazzler'; also *Amaryllis belladonna*.

Useful tip: Store dormant bulbs at a temperature above 15°C (60°F) to force into flower early.

HIPPEASTRUM 'LADY JANE'

Perhaps the most spectacular of all indoor bulbs, Hippeastrums can be forced into bloom in early winter in a living room without a preliminary period in darkness. If you continue caring for the plants after flowering, they will repeat their beautiful display of huge trumpets year after year.

37

Hoya Wax Flower

HOYA BELLA

Hoyas are tough easily grown house plants, despite their apparent fragility when in flower. The immaculate blooms are produced in large pendent clusters, and each fragrant waxy star has a drop of sweet nectar suspended at its centre. Never deadhead blooms when they fade as future flower clusters grow on the same stalks.

Positioning: Sunny window; avoid the hottest summer sunshine.

Season: Flowers late spring to early autumn.

Height: H. carnosa up to 3m (10ft); H. lanceolata 45cm (18in).

Spread: 45–60cm (18–24in) (H. lanceolata).

Care: Keep evenly moist spring to autumn, almost dry in winter. Mist regularly except when in bloom. Feed with high-potash fertilizer monthly when flowering. Repot young plants in spring in soil-based compost and top-dress mature ones: replace 5cm (2in) of compost. Do not move when in flower. Nip out growing tips occasionally.

Propagation: Grow tip cuttings in spring.

Recommended: H. carnosa, H. c. 'Variegata', 'Exotica'; H. lanceolata ssp. bella; H. multiflora.

Useful tip: To encourage prolific flowering, rest in a cool place in winter, feed very little and keep plants potbound.

Hypoestes Polka Dot Plant

Positioning: Best possible light; avoid hot summer sunshine. High humidity essential.

Season: Foliage all year.

Height: 30–60cm (1–2ft).

Spread: 30–60cm (1–2ft).

Care: Keep compost evenly moist from spring to autumn, reducing watering from late summer through winter. Do not let plants dry out. Mist leaves regularly. Apply fertilizer every 2–3 weeks from early summer to mid-autumn. Repot in spring in shallow pans of soil-less compost, and prune to keep compact. Pinch out summer flowers as they appear. Keep above 13°C (55°F) in winter.

Propagation: Grow tip cuttings in spring or summer.

Recommended: *H. phyllostachya*, syn. *H. sanguinolenta*, forms 'Carmina', 'Splash', 'Pupuriana', 'Wit'; *H. aristata*.

Useful tip: Plants are unsuitable for dry rooms.

HYPOESTES PHYLLOSTACHYA

This attractive and well-known foliage plant is grown for the brightly coloured spots and blotches on its soft downy leaves. Bright light ensures the most vivid colours, whereas shade turns the foliage green. Frequent pinching will produce satisfyingly bushy shrubs. *H. aristata* is a plain-leafed form with attractive rosy-purple flower spikes in late winter.

Impatiens Busy Lizzie

NEW GUINEA HYBRID

There are many lovely varieties, often grown outside as bedding plants for shady spots, but equally successful as house plants for bright window-sills, where they will flower over a long period. Try potting up bedding varieties in autumn to continue flowering indoors and provide cuttings the following spring.

Positioning: Very bright or sunny window-sill, shaded from hot midday sun.

Season: Flowers spring to autumn; all year if kept above 15°C (60°F) in winter.

Height: 45–60cm (18–24in).

Spread: 45–60cm (18–24in).

Care: Always keep compost moist but reduce frequency of watering in winter unless kept warm. Mist leaves occasionally. Apply fertilizer weekly while flowering. Repot in spring when very rootbound, in well-drained soil-based compost in plastic pots. Prune leggy stems to half their length in spring, pinch out growing tips. Ventilate well on hot days.

Propagation: Grow tip cuttings at any time.

Recommended: *I. walleriana* hybrids like Accent, Blitz and Tempo series; *I. hawkeri*, and New Guinea hybrids; *I. marianae*; *I. tinctoria*.

Useful tip: The brittle stems of taller plants may need staking.

Jasminum polyanthum Pink Jasmine

Positioning: Well-lit window-sill; some shade from the hottest sunshine.

Season: Flowers winter and early spring.

Size: Up to 90cm (3ft) high and wide on a hoop, more on canes or trained into a conservatory roof.

Care: Water liberally with rainwater during growth; keep just moist in winter. Mist leaves frequently. Apply fertilizer weekly while growing. Repot in early spring in soil-based compost. Prune lightly to shape; pinch tips regularly. Keep cool (about 7°C/45°F) from autumn until flowering begins.

Propagation: Grow tip cuttings in spring or summer.

Recommended: Basic species; also *J. officinale* and *affine*, 'Argenteovariegatum', 'Aureum'; *J. mesnyi*, syn. *J. primulinum*.

Useful tip: Plants may be grown in a greenhouse or conservatory, and brought indoors as flowering starts.

JASMINUM POLYANTHUM

This vigorous climber can scramble into the roof of a conservatory and will perfume the air in late winter with its numerous starry pinkish-white flowers. It is lovely in pots if trained around large wire or cane hoops.

41

Justicia brandegeeana Shrimp Plant

JUSTICIA BRANDEGEEANA

This is a popular subtropical shrub, easily grown in very good light where its extravagant prawn-shaped flower heads, up to 10cm (4in) long, will often cover the bushy plants completely. The true flowers, tiny and white, drop quickly but the salmon-pink bracts last for weeks. Several attractive relatives are also worth growing. (syn. *Beloperone guttata*.)

Positioning: Sunny window-sill, ideally warm by day, cool at night; shielded from strong sunshine.

Season: Flowers late spring to early autumn; all year in warm conditions.

Height: Up to 90cm (3ft).

Spread: 45–60cm (18–24in).

Care: Water generously from spring to late summer, then decrease watering gradually; plants must not dry out. Mist now and then. Apply fertilizer weekly from spring to autumn. Repot if needed in spring; cut plants back to half their size for bushy growth.

Propagation: Grow tip cuttings in spring or summer in a propagator.

Recommended: Basic species, and 'Yellow Queen', syn. *lutea*; *J. carnea*; *Dicliptera suberecta*, syn. *J. suberecta*; *Pachystachys lutea*, syn. *Beloperone* 'Super Goldy'.

Useful tip: Pinch the tips of young shoots a few times to encourage dense bushy growth.

Kalanchoe blossfeldiana Flaming Katy

Positioning: Near a bright window; some shade from hot midday sun. Full sun in winter.

Season: Flowers spring (winter with short-day treatment).

Height: 15–45cm (6–18in).

Spread: 15–30cm (6–12in).

Care: Water freely from spring to autumn, sparingly in winter; let the surface dry out between waterings. Apply fertilizer every 3–4 weeks from late spring to mid-autumn. Repot in late spring, in soil-based compost. For winter flowers keep plants in the dark for 15–16 hours daily, for 3–4 weeks from summer. Deadhead; prune to shape when blooms fade and keep dry for a month on a shaded window-sill.

Propagation: Grow tip cuttings in spring.

Recommended: Modern hybrids like 'Vesuvius', 'Vulcan'; seed mixtures like 'Lilliput', 'Tom Thumb'.

Useful tip: Bury several potted plants in a bowl of compost for a winter display.

KALANCHOE BLOSSFELDIANA

These popular plants, in various vivid shades of red, orange, yellow and lilac, are often bought in full flower in winter and then discarded. With little special care, they can be kept from one year to the next, either to flower naturally in spring or for forcing into winter bloom. The succulent leaves need full light, but react to hot sunshine by turning red.

43

KALANCHOE DAIGREMONTIANA

These Kalanchoes, once called Bryophyllum, are among the easiest succulent foliage plants to grow. They soon fill a pot with young plants because whole clusters of the plantlets they bear on their leaves spontaneously fall and root where they land.

Positioning: Warm sunny window-sill; avoid only the hottest sunshine.

Season: Foliage all year.

Height: Up to 60–90cm (2–3ft).

Spread: 30–45cm (12–18in).

Care: Water regularly with rainwater in summer; let compost dry between waterings; less water in winter if plants are kept cooler. Do not feed if plants are to remain compact; apply cactus fertilizer monthly in summer for stronger growth. Repot in spring if rootbound, in soil-based compost with added grit or sand. Stand outdoors in summer as fresh air is beneficial.

Propagation: Grow plantlets at any time.

Recommended: Basic species; also *K. laxiflora*, *K. l.* 'Fedtshenko', syn. *K. fedtshenkoi*, and 'Variegata'; *K. delagonensis*, syn. *K. tubiflora*.

Useful tip: Cooler conditions in winter produce more shapely plants.

Lantana camara   Yellow Sage, Shrub Verbena

Positioning: Bright as possible; plenty of sun except at midday in summer.

Season: Late spring to mid-autumn.

Height: 30–60cm (1–2ft), but may reach 1.5–1.8m (5–6ft).

Spread: 60–75cm (2–2½ft).

Care: Water freely from spring to autumn; sparingly in winter, but do not let compost dry out. Mist leaves now and then. Apply fertilizer every 2–3 weeks in summer and autumn. Repot every other year in spring in soil-less compost. Prune to shape after flowering. Keep warm in winter (minimum temperature 13°C/55°F).

Propagation: Grow tip cuttings in spring or summer.

Recommended: Basic species, and 'Brazier', 'Snow White', 'Mine d'Or', 'Mr Bessieres'; *L. montevidensis*, syn. *L. sellowiana*, and 'Malan's Gold', 'Snow Queen'.

Useful tip: Whitefly can be a threat in some years.

LANTANA CAMARA

Although unimpressive out of season, these plants are stunningly colourful over a long flowering period; their rounded clusters of tiny blooms open pale yellow or pink and change to clear red or deep orange. The plants are aromatic and, if stood outdoors, will attract large numbers of butterflies.

45

Maranta Prayer Plant

MARANTA LEUCONEURA VAR. ERYTHRONEURA

Marantas are familiar and very attractive foliage plants with distinctive, often vivid, leaf markings such as highlighted veins and prominent blotches in symmetrical rows. They can be difficult to keep in good condition because of their need for high humidity, but usually thrive in a glass case or bottle garden. Arrowroot is prepared from the roots of the 2m (6½ft) tall species *M. arundinacea*.

Positioning: Semi-shade (summer), light shade (winter); good light, constant humidity; protect from draughts. Keep warm in winter (minimum temperature 14°C/ 57°F).

Season: Foliage all year.

Height: 20–30cm (8–12in).

Spread: 30–60cm (12–24in).

Care: Keep very moist with room-temperature rainwater from spring to autumn; reduce watering slightly in winter. Spray foliage daily and stand young plants on pebbles in saucers of water. Apply fertilizer fortnightly from early summer to early autumn. Repot every 2 years in spring in shallow pots or bowls.

Propagation: Divide mature plants at repotting time.

Recommended: *M. leuconeura*, basic species and var. *erythroneura*, var. *kerchoveana*; *M. bicolor*; many forms of *Calathea*, *Ctenanthe*, *Stromanthe*.

Useful tip: Plants may be trained up moss-sticks.

Positioning: Light shade; good light, especially in winter. Allow room for plants to develop.

Season: Foliage all year.

Height: Up to 3m (10ft), more in a conservatory.

Spread: 1.8m (6ft).

Care: Water freely, ideally with tepid rainwater, from spring to early autumn; let the surface dry out between waterings. Reduce water in winter, especially when cool. Mist leaves regularly, and sponge from time to time. Apply fertilizer fortnightly in summer and autumn. Repot every 2 years in spring in soil-less compost and move plants on to larger pots; top-dress mature plants by replacing 5cm (2in) of compost.

Propagation: Pot up growing tips and their aerial roots in spring or summer.

Recommended: M. deliciosa, basic species, 'Variegata'; M. adansonii.

Useful tip: Train on moss-sticks; tuck aerial roots into them or compost; cut some off if necessary.

MONSTERA DELICIOSA

These handsome and distinctive plants need no introduction. The giant, deeply incised or perforated leaves can reach 45cm (18in) or more across, and the strong plants soon make impressively sculptural centrepieces that need plenty of room and sturdy support.

Nephrolepis Sword Fern

NEPHROLEPIS EXALTATA 'BOSTONIENSIS'

Vigorous and graceful at all times, the sword ferns are some of the loveliest foliage plants for moist shade. They come from tropical forests, so try to imitate the dappled shade and even dampness they are used to – self-watering pots often provide ideal conditions.

Positioning: Fairly well-lit; avoid direct sunshine, dry positions, draughts.

Season: Foliage all year.

Height: 30–75cm (12–30in).

Spread: 45–90cm (18–36in) or more.

Care: Water regularly with rainwater in spring and summer, otherwise less often; do not let plants dry out or become waterlogged. Spray leaves regularly and stand plants on moist pebbles. Apply quarter-strength fertilizer at every spring and summer watering. Repot in spring, in ericaceous compost. Cut off withered fronds cleanly at their bases.

Propagation: Separate plantlets from their runners in summer and pot up.

Recommended: *N. exaltata* and 'Bostoniensis', 'Rooseveltii', 'Smithii', 'Teddy Junior'; *N. cordifolia* and 'Plumosa'.

Useful tip: A nearby table-lamp will counter leaf-drop caused by too much shade.

Positioning: Well-lit and ventilated; away from heat and the strongest sunshine.

Season: Fruits late summer to early winter.

Height: 8–15cm (3–6in).

Spread: 15–20cm (6–8in).

Care: Keep constantly moist; water freely spring to autumn, more sparsely in winter. Apply half-strength fertilizer every 6–8 weeks in spring and summer. Repot in spring in soil-based compost in shallow pans; water cautiously until new growth appears. Stand plants outdoors from late spring in a cool place (maximum 13°C/ 55°F); bring indoors when berries start to colour in late summer. Keep in a cool room or cold frame for the winter.

Propagation: Divide plants at repotting time.

Recommended: *N. granadensis*, syn. *N. depressa*; *N. balfouriana*; *Soleirolia*, syn. *Helxine*, best form *S. soleirolii* 'Aurea'.

Useful tip: Cool conditions are essential at all times.

NERTERA DEPRESSA

These creeping plants are perennial and last for several years with little attention. The dense mats of tiny leaves are covered in minute greenish-white flowers in early summer, followed by masses of bright pea-sized berries which last for months. As mountain species from the southern hemisphere, plants survive surprisingly low temperatures, and may even be grown in a frost-free cold frame once the display of berries is over.

Opuntia Prickly Pear

OPUNTIA MICRODASYS

Opuntias develop as chains of spiny pads that grow unpredictably in all directions. For plants to flower, they need sunny summers, cool winters and almost potbound conditions; fruits are rarely formed indoors, however. As well as their more conspicuous thorns, pads sport tufts of tiny barbed spines or 'glochids' – beware of these, for they can break at a touch and cause great pain.

Positioning: Sunny window-sill or conservatory in summer.

Season: Foliage all year.

Height: 30cm–1.5m (1–5ft) high, according to species.

Spread: 23–60cm (9–24in).

Care: Keep fairly moist from mid-spring to early autumn, almost dry otherwise. Apply cactus fertilizer monthly in spring and summer. Repot in spring in half-pots of cactus or gritty soil-based compost (wear gloves for this). Cooler position (minimum 4°C/40°F) in winter. Prune one or two older stems occasionally to prevent leggy growth.

Propagation: Grow from mature pads in spring or summer.

Recommended: *O. bergeriana*; also *O. lindheimeri*; *O. microdasys* and *O. m.* 'Albispina'.

Useful tip: Joints between old pads normally become corky; if they start shrivelling in warm winter quarters more water is needed.

Palmae Palms

Positioning: Semi- or light shade; avoid very dry rooms, draughts.

Season: Foliage all year.

Height: 1.8–2.4m (6–8ft) or more.

Spread: 1.2–1.8m (4–6ft).

Care: Water moderately, ideally with room-temperature rainwater, in spring and summer, otherwise sparingly. Mist regularly; occasionally sponge mature leaves. Apply fertilizer monthly in spring and summer. Repot in spring in well-drained soil-less compost in deep pots, only when rootbound; otherwise replace the top 5cm (2in) of compost. Cut off ageing brown leaves.

Propagation: Difficult; sow fresh seeds in spring.

Recommended: *Howea forsteriana; H. belmoreana; Chamaedorea elegans; Syagrus cocoides; Phoenix dactylifera; P. roebelinii; P. canariensis.*

Useful tip: Pot firmly and avoid disturbing roots.

CHAMAEDOREA ELEGANS

All palms are very handsome foliage house plants and easy to care for. Larger species are dramatic in shaded corners, while dwarf forms are perfect for bottle gardens and terrariums. They are expensive to buy because they are difficult to raise and usually grow slowly.

Pelargonium (foliage) Scented-leafed Geranium

PELARGONIUM RADULA GROUP

Unlike other Pelargoniums, these endearing plants have woody shrub-like stems and small pale flowers in summer that are fairly insignificant compared to the beauty of the aromatic foliage. Crushing or rubbing the crinkled, divided or variegated leaves releases fragrances as varied as citrus, mint, pine or cinnamon.

Positioning: Bright; sunshine but shield from hot midday sun. Keep cool (7°C/45°F) in winter.

Season: Foliage all year.

Height: Up to 1.2m (4ft).

Spread: 60–90cm (2–3ft).

Care: Water freely spring to mid-autumn; let the surface dry out between waterings. Keep moist in winter. Apply half-strength high-potash fertilizer every 4–6 weeks mid-spring to mid-autumn. Repot every 2–3 years in early spring in gritty soil-based compost; prune to shape. Pinch out growing tips now and then.

Propagation: Grow tip cuttings from side-shoots in late summer under glass.

Recommended: *P. odoratissimum*; *P. graveolens*; *P. tomentosum*; *P. crispum* and 'Variegatum', 'Peach Cream'; *P. capitatum*; *P. fragrans*; 'Attar of Roses', 'Prince of Orange', 'Chocolate Peppermint'.

Useful tip: Watch out for greenfly and aphids.

Pelargonium × domesticum Regal Pelargonium

Positioning: Sunny window-sill; warm in summer, cooler in winter (8–10°C/46–50°F).

Season: Flowers spring to mid-summer.

Height: 30–75cm (12–30in).

Spread: 30–45cm (12–18in).

Care: Soak well then leave until compost is almost dry before watering again. Water less frequently in winter. Apply high-potash fertilizer every 2–3 weeks, spring to early autumn. Repot in spring in soil-based compost. Pinch out growing tips several times. Deadhead; shorten exhausted stems by one-third after flowering.

Propagation: Grow tip cuttings in late summer.

Recommended: 'Aztec', 'Brown's Butterfly', 'Elsie Hickman', 'Pompeii', 'Carisbrooke', 'Grand Slam', 'Grossmutter Fischer', 'La Paloma', 'White Chiffon'.

Useful tip: Continue watering and feeding when flowers have faded; this will encourage side-shoots for cuttings.

PELARGONIUM × DOMESTICUM 'MULTIFLORUM'

These gorgeous hybrids deserve centre-stage positions when covered with their waved and frilled funnel-shaped blooms, which are often in startling colour combinations and prominently marked like orchids. The best flowers appear on one- or two-year-old plants, so propagate regularly from cuttings.

53

Pelargonium × hortorum Zonal Geranium

ZONAL GERANIUM HYBRID

Geraniums are among the easiest house plants to grow and keep from one year to the next, with an enormous variety of form and habit: ivy-leafed kinds trail languidly, while some zonals (named after the distinct dark leaf marking) can tower up to the ceiling. There are single, double and rosebud flowers, in many shades. All are worth growing.

Positioning: Well-lit window-sill; full sunshine for much of the day. Keep cool in winter (minimum 7°C/ 45°F.)

Season: Flowers early summer to early winter.

Height: 30cm–1.8m (1–6ft).

Spread: 23–60cm (9–24in).

Care: Water freely from spring to autumn; let compost dry out between waterings. Keep barely moist in winter. Apply fertilizer every 3–4 weeks in summer and autumn. Repot in early spring in well-drained soil-based compost. Trim the rootball to fit a smaller pot than previously. Pinch out growing tips once or twice. Pot on as necessary. Deadhead; remove yellow leaves.

Propagation: Grow tip cuttings in late summer.

Recommended: 'Appleblossom', 'Black Vesuvius', 'Festiva Maxima', 'Mrs Henry Cox', 'Paul Crampel'.

Useful tip: Plants are semi-succulent, so avoid over-watering.

Peperomia Peperomia

Positioning: Well-lit; avoid direct sunlight, draughts and sudden temperature changes.

Season: Foliage all year.

Height: 15–30cm (6–12in).

Spread: 15–45cm (6–18in).

Care: Water from below. Just moisten compost with tepid rainwater in spring and summer; let the surface dry between waterings. Give very little in winter. Mist leaves now and then during growth; keep foliage quite dry in winter. Apply half-strength fertilizer monthly in spring and summer. Repot in half-pots of soil-less compost in spring every 3–4 years.

Propagation: Grow tip or leaf cuttings in spring and summer.

Recommended: *P. caperata*, basic species, 'Variegata'; *P. magnoliifolia*, *P. m.* 'Golden Gate', 'USA'; *P. argyreia*; *P. scandens* (trailing), *P. s.* 'Variegata'.

Useful tip: Cut off bruised leaves cleanly with a sharp knife.

PEPEROMIA CAPERATA 'LUNA RED'

These popular tropical plants are easy to grow under normal room conditions provided you avoid over-watering, especially in winter. They are shallow-rooted and long-lived plants, some bushy and others trailing, with semi-succulent foliage that remains colourful at all seasons. The flowers are insignificant and may be removed.

Philodendron

PHILODENDRON SCANDENS

Positioning:	Semi-shade or good light; avoid direct sunshine. Keep above 10°C (50°F) in winter.
Season:	Foliage all year.
Height:	1.8m (6ft) or more.
Spread:	60–120cm (2–4ft).
Care:	Keep evenly moist, ideally with tepid rainwater, in spring and summer; drier in autumn, winter. Mist leaves regularly, sponge larger ones now and then. Apply high-potash fertilizer fortnightly in spring, summer. Repot in spring in soil-less compost, young plants annually, mature ones every 2–3 years. Cut back to size in early spring; regularly pinch out growing tips.
Propagation:	Grow tip cuttings in spring and summer.
Recommended:	*P. angustisectum*; *P. erubescens*, *P. e.* 'Burgundy', 'Imperial Red', 'Red Emerald'; *P. scandens*; hybrids like 'Emerald Queen', 'New Red'.
Useful tip:	Keep variegated forms near a window.

Philodendrons are traditional foliage house plants that can survive some neglect. Most are natural climbers or trailers, and may be grown to a great height, adding a lush tropical atmosphere to a lightly shaded corner. Aerial roots are often formed, and these should be pushed into the compost or a supporting moss-stick to help sustain upper leaves.

Positioning: Well-lit window-sill; avoid direct sunlight, draughts. Tolerates winter temperatures of 12°C (54°F).

Season: Foliage all year.

Height: Up to 38cm (15in).

Spread: 30–45cm (12–18in).

Care: Water freely, with tepid water, from spring to autumn; let the surface dry out between waterings. Give very little in winter. Mist leaves now and then (stop if black patches appear). Apply high-potash fertilizer fortnightly in spring and summer. In spring repot in shallow pans of soil-based compost and cut back to shape if necessary. Pinch out growing tips.

Propagation: Grow tip cuttings in late spring.

Recommended: P. cadieri, dwarf 'Minima'; P. repens; P. nummulariifolia; P. involucrata, P. i. 'Moon Valley', 'Norfolk' and 'Silver Tree'; P. microphylla.

Useful tip: Watch out for aphids and red spider mites in summer.

PILEA CADIERI 'MOON VALLEY'

Most of these very easy and attractive foliage plants have deeply quilted leaves brightly marked in shades of olive green, copper, purple or silver, and often highlighted by red or purple veins. *P. microphylla* (artillery plant) is quite different, its soft pale foliage and bushy habit resembling a typical fern. Plants eventually become gaunt and leggy, so regular propagation is advisable.

Plectranthus Swedish Ivy

PLECTRANTHUS COLEOIDES 'MARGINATUS'

These simple, easy-going plants tolerate dry living-room conditions and even occasional neglect. With their long stems and attractive evergreen foliage, they are ideal for hanging baskets and also as ground cover at the base of large pot plants. The occasional blue or white flowers, which resemble those of Coleus (*Solenostemon*), are insignificant and can be removed.

Positioning: Good light or semi-shade; on a sunless window-sill.

Season: Foliage all year.

Size: Trails to 90cm (3ft); 30–45cm (12–18in) wide.

Care: Keep evenly moist from spring to autumn; water sparingly in winter unless kept in warmth (10°C/50°F). Mist leaves now and then. Apply fertilizer 2–3 times in summer. Repot in soil-less compost in spring, again in early or mid-summer to produce large plants. Allow to trail or pinch tips regularly to keep bushy.

Propagation: Grow tip cuttings in spring or summer.

Recommended: *P. forsteri*, syn. *P. coleoides*, and *P. f.* 'Marginatus'; *P. madagascariensis*, 'Variegated Mintleaf'; *P. oertendahlii* and 'Variegatus'; *P. thyrsoideus*.

Useful tip: Stems soon become leggy, so take cuttings regularly.

Pleione Indian Crocus, Window-sill Orchid

Positioning: Well-lit window-sill; avoid direct sunshine, draughts. Good ventilation in summer. Move when frost threatens.

Season: Flowers in summer.

Height: 10–15cm (4–6in).

Spread: 8–10cm (3–4in).

Care: Water liberally with tepid rainwater in spring and summer; less in autumn, none in winter. Apply general or orchid fertilizer fortnightly from spring to early autumn. Repot in spring in orchid compost in half-pots. Mist leaves now and then when not in flower. Water and feed until leaves die down, then keep cool and dry until spring.

Propagation: Separate and pot up pseudo-bulbs at repotting time.

Recommended: *P. bulbocodioides* and Limprichtii Group; *P. formosana* and 'Alba', 'Lilac Beauty', 'Ruby Throat'; *P. praecox* and Shantung 'Muriel Harberd'; *P. speciosa*.

Useful tip: Plants may not flower in insufficient light.

PLEIONE FORMOSANA

Perhaps the easiest orchids for growing as house plants, Pleiones are almost hardy enough to grow outdoors and can survive winter temperatures as low as 5°C (41°F). There are many forms, all dwarf and producing pink, white or rosy-purple 5–10cm (2–4in) blooms with extravagant markings and fringed lips.

Pteris

PTERIS ENSIFORMIS

These very varied ferns cannot tolerate dry air or neglect, but otherwise they are some of the easiest to grow well indoors. Plain, crested and variegated forms are all popular, both as specimen plants and for combining with other house plants in mixed bowls – an arrangement that helps to sustain the high humidity the ferns prefer. Green forms enjoy the cool moist shade under greenhouse benches, where they will often spread from spores.

Positioning: Light even shade near a sunless window; with good light in winter. Variegated kinds prefer temperatures of at least 15°C (60°F).

Season: Foliage all year.

Height: 30–90cm (1–3ft).

Spread: 45–75cm (18–30in).

Care: Always keep compost moist. Water liberally with rainwater from spring to early autumn. Reduce watering from mid- or late autumn onwards to a level consistent with the room temperature. Apply half-strength fertilizer weekly in spring and summer. Repot in spring in plastic half-pots of soil-less compost. Spray plants regularly and stand on pebbles in trays of water.

Propagation: Divide when repotting.

Recommended: P. ensiformis, basic species, 'Victoriae'; P. tremula; P. argyrea; P. cretica, basic species, 'Albolineata', 'Gaultherii', 'Wilsonii', 'Whimsettii'.

Useful tip: In winter keep in a cool bedroom, away from warm dry air.

Rhododendron simsii Indian Azalea

Positioning: Good light; some direct sunshine. Living room while flowering; otherwise keep cool, away from radiators.

Season: Flowers winter and early spring.

Height: 30–45cm (12–18in).

Spread: 38–60cm (15–24in).

Care: Always keep moist with rainwater. Mist leaves regularly while flowering. Apply rhododendron fertilizer every 2–3 weeks in spring and summer. Keep cool and frost-free from the end of flowering until early autumn. Repot in ericaceous compost in plastic pots about a month after flowering. Remove faded blooms between flowering and repotting time; cut off shoots or shorten them by half.

Propagation: Grow vigorous tip cuttings in spring or late summer.

Recommended: Plants are bought by colour and not name.

Useful tip: Buy a plant with plenty of buds, ideally single stemmed, if you intend to keep it when flowering ceases.

AZALEA HYBRID

These lovely plants are sometimes discarded after flowering. If properly tended for the rest of the year, however, they may be brought into bloom again annually for many years, giving weeks of lavish colour just when it is most appreciated. Drought and excessive warmth can be lethal. (syn. *Azalea indica*.)

RHOICISSUS RHOMBOIDEA 'ELLEN DANICA'

Grape ivies are luxuriant climbers that thrive in cooler, shady corners in the home where they develop into glossy columns of richly coloured foliage that is also effective when allowed to trail gracefully.

Positioning: Reasonably well-lit: a hall, corridor or stairwell. Allow room for growth. Minimum winter temperature 7°C (45°F).

Season: Foliage all year.

Height: 3m (10ft) or more.

Spread: 45cm (18in).

Care: Water liberally from spring to autumn, more sparsely in winter. Mist or sponge leaves now and then (often in warm conditions). Apply fertilizer weekly from the appearance of new shoots to late summer. Repot in spring if rootbound, in well-drained soil-based compost. Tie growing stems on trellis, canes or moss-sticks.

Propagation: Grow tip cuttings in spring or late summer, in groups of three.

Recommended: *R. capensis,* syn. *Cissus capensis; R. rhomboidea,* syn. *Cissus rhombifolia,* form 'Ellen Danica'.

Useful tip: Grow in a hanging basket in a bathroom or conservatory for an impressive display.

Saintpaulia African Violet

Positioning: Good light, away from direct sunshine. Avoid temperature changes, radiators, draughts.

Season: Mainly summer, but sometimes several flushes of bloom throughout the year.

Height: Up to 15cm (6in).

Spread: 10–20cm (4–8in).

Care: Keep compost moist with tepid rainwater; let the surface dry between waterings. Do not wet the foliage. Stand on pebbles in saucers of water. Apply half-strength high-potash or African violet fertilizer monthly in spring and summer. Repot in spring, in ericaceous compost, in shallow plastic pots or pans. Deadhead; remove damaged leaves and their stalks.

Propagation: Divide mature plants at repotting time.

Recommended: Rhapsodie, Rococo strains, 'Chimera', 'Blue Border', 'Love Bug', 'Pip Squeak', 'Breezy Blue'.

Useful tip: Plants need bright natural or artificial light to maintain winter flowering.

SAINTPAULIA HYBRID

African violets are perhaps the most popular of all house plants and many thousands of lovely varieties are available, from large standard types, some with prettily variegated leaves, to dainty miniatures and trailing kinds. With care they will bloom almost continuously, in a wide range of colours and attractive flower forms. Beware of fertilizers with a high nitrogen content as they can discourage flowering.

Sansevieria Mother-in-law's Tongue

SANSEVIERIA TRIFASCIATA 'AURENTII'

Almost indestructible in the home, these familiar house plants are desert species that tolerate considerable neglect; only low temperatures and over-watering causes them any serious distress. The foliage is bold and semi-succulent, an ideal foil for flowering house plants.

Positioning: In or near a bright window; full sunshine most of the day. Some light shade tolerated. Keep warm; minimum 10°C (50°F) in winter.

Season: All year round; small flowers in late spring.

Height: Up to 90cm (3ft).

Spread: 30cm (12in).

Care: Keep just moist in spring, summer; let surface dry between waterings. Do not wet the leaves and heart. Keep almost dry in autumn, winter. Apply high-potash or cactus fertilizer every 3–4 weeks in spring, summer. Repot in spring if rootbound, in free-draining soil-based or cactus compost in clay pots.

Propagation: Divide mature plants in spring.

Recommended: *S. trifasciata* and 'Laurentii'; dwarf 'Hahnii', syn. *S. hahnii*, 'Golden Hahnii', 'Silver Hahnii'.

Useful tip: Check a mature plant's root growth now and then; plants prefer to be potbound, but will eventually break their containers.

Schefflera Ivy Tree, Umbrella Tree

Positioning: Well-lit; out of direct sunshine, draughts. Plants can adapt to light shade. Avoid too much warmth.

Season: Foliage all year.

Height: Up to 3m (10ft).

Spread: 90cm (3ft) or more.

Care: Keep evenly moist in spring, summer; let the surface dry between waterings; mist leaves frequently. Water sparingly in autumn, winter. Apply fertilizer monthly in spring, summer. Repot in spring in soil-based compost in large plastic containers (young plants twice in their first year). Fresh air is essential during growth.

Propagation: Difficult; grow tip cuttings in spring with rooting hormone.

Recommended: *S. actinophylla*; *S. arboricola* basic species, 'Compacta', 'Gold Capella'; *S. heptaphylla*, syn. *S. octophylla*; *S. digitata*.

Useful tip: Leaves sometimes fall in winter, but new growth reappears in spring.

SCHEFFLERA ARBORICOLA 'GOLD CAPELLA'

Schefflera are striking evergreen trees that can reach 30m (100ft) in their natural habitat, but remain attractive glossy-leafed shrubs for several years in the home. Although tropical plants, they come from high altitudes and are best suited to a hall or staircase, rather than a warm living room. (syn. *Brassaia*.)

Schlumbergera Christmas cactus

SCHLUMBERGERA TRUNCATA

These beautiful winter-flowering plants colonize trees in tropical forests and so prefer to grow in fibrous compost with plenty of water at certain times. The secret of prolific flowering is to give plants two cool dry rests each year to stimulate buds to form. (syns. *S. truncata*, *Zygocactus truncatus*.)

Positioning: Well-lit; shaded from full sunshine. After last frosts move to light shade outdoors until early autumn.

Season: Flowers in winter.

Height: 23–30cm (9–12in).

Spread: Up to 60cm (2ft).

Care: Keep evenly moist with tepid rainwater and mist leaves while flowering, then keep almost dry for 2 months. Water regularly while outdoors; protect from slugs. After bringing plants indoors keep cool and almost dry; increase watering and warmth when buds form. Apply cactus fertilizer except when dry. Repot after spring rest, in orchid or soil-less compost; young plants annually, mature specimens every 3–4 years.

Propagation: Pot up pairs of pads in spring.

Recommended: Over 200 desirable varieties. Also *Hatiora gaertneri* (flowers mid- to late spring).

Useful tip: Buds may fall off if plants are moved after flowers start to form.

Scindapsus Devil's Ivy

Positioning: Light shade; avoid direct sunlight, abrupt temperature drops to below 13°C (55°F), cold draughts.

Season: Foliage all year.

Height: Up to 2m (6½ft).

Spread: 45–60cm (18–24in).

Care: Keep moist, ideally with rainwater, from spring to early autumn; let the surface dry between waterings. Water sparingly at other times. Apply fertilizer fortnightly in spring, summer. Repot in spring in well-drained soil-based compost. Pinch out tips for bushy growth, or tie stems, aerial roots to trellis or a moss-stick.

Propagation: Grow tip cuttings in spring or summer.

Recommended: *S. aureus* (syns. *Epipremnum aureum*, *Rhaphidophora aurea*), basic species, 'Golden Queen', 'Marble Queen'; *S. pictus* and 'Argyraeus'.

Useful tip: Trail plants from a pot or grow unstopped in hanging baskets.

SCINDAPSUS AUREUS

These highly ornamental climbers or trailers have glossy heart-shaped leaves and a lively pattern of gold speckles in the basic species. The better-known gold and white varieties need a little more warmth, light and humidity. Although most kinds are now classed as *Epipremnum*, they are still widely sold under their old names.

Sedum Stonecrop

SEDUM PACHYPHYLLUM

Sedum are unusual and very varied succulents. They often have pretty star-shaped flowers but are usually grown for the symmetry and beautiful colours of their fleshy leaves, in which they store moisture. They do not require much heat, and in summer are best kept outdoors or in a very well-ventilated window; trailing kinds are effective in hanging baskets. Over-watering, especially in cool conditions, may cause plants to rot.

Positioning: Sunny window-sill; keep cooler and in good light in winter.

Season: Foliage all year; occasional flowers in spring.

Height: 15–30cm (6–12in); trailing types up to 90cm (3ft) long.

Spread: 30cm (12in).

Care: Apply tepid water when compost is fairly dry, every 1–2 months in winter, more often in summer. Apply half-strength fertilizer monthly in summer. Repot in spring in well-drained cactus or soil-based compost in pans or half-pots.

Propagation: Pot up leaves that drop and root spontaneously any time.

Recommended: S. morganianum; S. bellum; S. sieboldii 'Mediovariegatum'; S. pachyphyllum; S. rubrotinctum and 'Ruby Glow', 'Aurora'.

Useful tip: For compact growth stand plants outdoors in a sheltered position in summer; bring indoors before nights turn cool and damp.

Senecio cruentus Cineraria

Positioning: Cool, well-lit; away from direct sunshine, draughts.

Season: Flowers late winter and spring.

Size: 20–60cm (8–24in) high and wide according to the strain.

Care: Keep cool, maximum (13°C/55°F) and evenly moist while flowering; plunge the pot into a bucket of tepid water whenever the surface dries out. Keep a little drier after flowering. Apply half-strength high-potash fertilizer monthly during growth and flowering. Cut each branch back to about 5cm (2in) long after flowering; rest plants in cool dry conditions until new growth appears.

Propagation: Pot up side-shoots in summer.

Recommended: Many fine strains, from Erfurt Dwarf (20cm/8in high) to Star and Exhibition mixtures (60cm/2ft high).

Useful tip: S. rowleyanus (String of Beads) is a popular trailing succulent with strings of pea-like leaves.

CINERARIA HYBRID

In the right conditions – cool at all times – Cinerarias produce a good head of daisy-like spring flowers in an impressive range of showy colours, held in broad trusses above the soft bushy foliage. Although often grown as annual flowers they are perennials and may be perpetuated from cuttings. (syn. *Pericallis × hybrida*.)

GLOXINIA HYBRID

Gloxinias were traditionally grown in hothouses and if they are given plenty of warmth and humidity these old-fashioned South American house plants give a striking display of 8cm (3in) blooms in opulent shades of red, purple and white for 2–3 months. With care they may be kept from one year to the next and will grow in strength and peformance.

Positioning: Near a well-lit window; avoid direct sunshine, draughts, dry rooms.

Season: Flowers late spring to late summer.

Height: 25–30cm (10–12in).

Spread: Up to 45cm (18in).

Care: Keep moist with tepid rainwater during growth and apply fertilizer at every watering; immerse plants in water if foliage wilts. Leave to grow for a few weeks after flowering then reduce watering to dry off in early autumn. Keep dormant tubers dry in pots at about 10°C (50°F); repot in ericaceous compost in late winter or early spring. Keep at 20°C (68°F); stand on moist pebbles. Thin shoots to leave the 2 or 3 strongest.

Propagation: Take cuttings in early summer.

Recommended: 'Duke of York', 'Etoile de Feu', 'Mont Blanc', 'Royal Pink', 'Violacea'; S. leucotricha.

Useful tip: Plant tubers hollow-sides-up, level with the compost surface.

Solanum   Winter Cherry, (False) Jerusalem Cherry

SOLANUM

Positioning: A sunny window.

Season: Flowers in summer; fruits autumn, winter.

Height: 30–60cm (1–2ft).

Spread: 30–60cm (1–2ft).

Care: Always keep moist: water liberally but keep plants a little drier (and cooler) than normal for 6–8 weeks after fruits fall. Mist plants when flowering. Apply high-potash fertilizer fortnightly in summer, autumn. Prune all branches back to half their length after fruiting. Repot in soil-less compost when new shoots appear; keep cool until late spring.

Propagation: Sow seeds in late winter or early spring.

Recommended: S. capsicastrum 'Craigii', 'Nanum', 'Variegatum'; S. pseudocapsicum, syn. S. hendersonii, and 'New Patterson', 'Red Giant'.

Useful tip: Plants can be moved to a sunny sheltered spot outdoors in spring for flowering and pollination. Bring indoors in autumn.

PSEUDOCAPSICUM 'THURINO'

These easily grown plants add a festive air to winter displays indoors. In summer and autumn they are covered with tiny white star-shaped flowers, followed by bright berries. These are usually orange-red but sometimes white or yellow, and last for 2–3 months or more, standing out vividly against the rich green, wavy-edged leaves. All berries are poisonous.

Solenostemon scutellarioides Flame Nettle

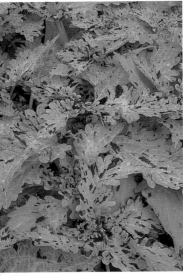

COLEUS HYBRID

These gorgeous foliage plants quickly develop into neat bushes in a wide range of startling colours, often with fantastic markings. They are usually raised from seed in spring, but an increasing number of named varieties are propagated by cuttings only and are favourites with collectors. (syn. *Coleus blumei*.)

Positioning: Bright window-sill or conservatory; some shade from midday sun.

Season: Foliage all year.

Height: 30–60cm (12–24in).

Spread: 45cm (18in).

Care: Always keep moist with rainwater. Daily watering may be necessary in summer. Apply high-potash fertilizer weekly from spring to autumn. Repot in spring in soil-less compost and cut plants back to half their height. Pinch out tips several times; remove flower spikes as they appear. Watch out for whitefly.

Propagation: Grow tip cuttings in spring or summer.

Recommended: 'Rainbow', 'Sabre', 'Wizard' mixtures and single colours 'Red Velvet', 'Salmon Lace', 'Volcano'; named varieties like 'Black Prince', 'Crimson Ruffles', 'Pineapple Beauty', 'Red Paisley Shawl', 'White Gem'.

Useful tip: For the best plants, take cuttings each year and treat as annuals. Mist leaves regularly.

Sparmannia African Hemp

Positioning: Well-lit, plenty of room; avoid direct sun except in winter when maximum sunlight encourages flowering.

Season: Foliage all year; flowers all spring.

Height: 90cm–1.8m (3–6ft).

Spread: Up to 1.2m (4ft).

Care: Water liberally in summer and autumn; a little less in winter. Keep plants dry for a month after flowering. Apply fertilizer weekly during growth until late summer. Repot annually after flowering (large plants in late summer) in soil-based compost in plastic containers and cut back to about 30cm (12in) high. Watch out for aphids and whitefly.

Propagation: Grow cuttings from side-shoots on flowering stems in spring.

Recommended: *S. africana*, basic species, 'Flore Pleno', 'Nana', 'Variegata'.

Useful tip: Light rather than hard pruning after flowering sometimes stimulates repeat blooming.

SPARMANNIA AFRICANA

Sparmannia is a handsome and fast-growing shrub for a conservatory or a well-lit corner of a large room, with softly hairy heart-shaped leaves that are attractive at all times. The gold-centred white flowers, up to 5cm (2in) across, appear in long-stalked clusters from late winter onwards. 'Nana' is a more compact table plant.

Spathiphyllum Peace Lily, White Sails

SPATHIPHYLLUM WALLISII

Peace lilies grow into graceful plants in a warm and lightly shaded living room. Their elegant lance-shaped leaves rise on tall stems from below the surface and are attractive all year. The white, lightly fragrant 8cm (3in) flowers resemble the spathes of arum lilies; they last for many weeks and often appear in several flushes.

Positioning: Lightly shaded window-sill; brighter light in winter. Avoid draughts, keep warm.

Season: Foliage all year; flowers in spring, summer and occasionally autumn.

Height: 30–45cm (12–18in).

Spread: 30–45cm (12–18in).

Care: Always keep moist: water lavishly with tepid water from spring to autumn, moderately in winter. Mist plants regularly, less in winter when they may go dormant. Sponge leaves now and then. Stand on pebbles in trays of water. Apply fertilizer fortnightly in spring, summer. In spring repot in plastic pots of soil-less compost.

Propagation: Divide mature plants at repotting time.

Recommended: *S. wallisii*, basic species; *S. patinii*; *S. floribundum*, best forms 'Mauna Loa', 'Mauna Loa Supreme'; 'Adagio', 'Petite', 'Tasson', 'Viscount'.

Useful tip: Plants often grow more luxuriantly in a warm humid conservatory.

Stephanotis floribunda Wax Flower, Madagascar Jasmine

Positioning: Best possible light, especially in winter; avoid direct summer sunshine. Keep cool in winter (maximum 13°C/55°F).

Season: Flowers in summer.

Height: Up to 3m (10ft).

Spread: 45cm (18in).

Care: Keep moderately moist with tepid rainwater from spring to autumn; a little drier in winter. Mist leaves occasionally. Apply fertilizer fortnightly in spring, summer. Repot in spring in well-drained rich soil-based compost. Support growing stems on trellis or twine them round a wire hoop. Do not move once buds start to appear as this will cause them to drop. Cut back to shape after flowering.

Propagation: Grow cuttings in spring from the previous year's wood.

Recommended: Basic species only.

Useful tip: Watch out for scale, mealy bug and red spider mite, especially in warm dry conditions.

STEPHANOTIS FLORIBUNDA

The heady perfume of its pure white waxy blooms is the great joy of this sensitive climber. It is the only species normally grown and although plants are not easy to grow well and keep healthy from one year to the next, in the right position they can develop into tall leafy specimens, quite breathtaking when covered with flowers.

Streptocarpus Cape Primrose

STREPTOCARPUS HYBRID

From the central veins of the long and straggly leaves of the Cape primrose, a succession of brightly coloured trumpet-shaped flowers rise on long stalks to give a fine display over a very long season – which may be extended with the aid of artificial light. It is easy to raise new plants from cuttings as replacements for flowering plants – which are at their best when two years old.

Positioning: In or near a well-lit window, shaded from the strongest sunshine. Keep fairly warm in winter; avoid draughts.

Season: Flowers late spring to early autumn.

Height: 15–30cm (6–12in).

Spread: 30–45cm (12–18in).

Care: Keep evenly moist, ideally with rainwater, from spring to early autumn; let the surface dry between waterings. Keep almost dry in winter. Apply half-strength fertilizer in spring, summer. Repot in spring in soil-based compost in shallow pots; water well. Deadhead flowers with their stalks; remove exhausted older leaves. After flowering, cut off large old leaves, pack plants close together and move to a bedroom until repotting time.

Propagation: Divide plants at repotting time.

Recommended: 'Constant Nymph'; also seed mixtures like 'Wiesmoor'.

Useful tip: Blooms may be cut and last well in water.

Tolmiea menziesii   Piggyback Plant

Positioning: Almost anywhere except in full sunshine; keep cooler in winter, minimum (10°C/50°F).

Season: Foliage all year.

Height: 23cm (9in).

Spread: Up to 45cm (18in).

Care: Always keep moist. Large plants need plenty of water and may be plunged into a bucket of water regularly in spring and summer. Reduce watering in autumn and winter according to the temperature. Mist leaves now and then in warm or dry conditions. Apply fertilizer fortnightly in spring, summer. Repot in spring in soil-less compost in plastic pots. Trim plants at any time to restore size or remove straggly stems.

Propagation: Divide mature plants at repotting time.

Recommended: Basic species and 'Taff's Gold', syns. 'Goldsplash', 'Maculata', and 'Variegata'.

Useful tip: Plants thrive in hanging baskets in shaded windows.

TOLMIEA MENZIESII

This is one of the easiest of all foliage house plants. It soon produces a leafy mass of downy bright leaves, each of which develops a tiny plantlet on its upper surface. The weight of these forces the arching stalks down to compost level, where the plantlets will root giving mature specimens a trailing appearance. Plants are almost hardy and may be attempted outdoors in a warm sheltered position.

Tradescantia Spiderwort

TRADESCANTIA FLUMINENSIS

Tradescantias are the best known members of a family of very similar creeping or trailing species. All are undemanding foliage plants with colourful leaf markings and a vigorous branching habit that makes them perfect subjects for hanging baskets indoors – and outside in summer. They are extremely easy to grow and withstand regular cutting back to shape; renew plants from cuttings when colours deteriorate.

Positioning: Well-lit; in a pot, bowl, hanging basket or below larger plants. Avoid temperatures below 10°C (50°F).

Season: Foliage all year.

Size: Trails to 60cm (2ft) or more.

Care: Water regularly in spring and summer; let surface dry between waterings. Reduce watering in autumn and winter, especially in a cool room. Mist occasionally. Apply fertilizer fortnightly in spring, summer. Repot in spring in soil-less compost in plastic pots or hanging baskets and cut back mature plants. Pinch out growing tips regularly; leave stems to trail.

Propagation: Grow cuttings any time except winter.

Recommended: *T. x andersoniana*; *T. cerinthoides*, syn. *T. blossfeldiana* 'Variegata'; coloured forms of *Callisia*, *Setcreasea*, *Zebrina*; white and cream forms of *T. fluminensis*.

Useful tip: Excessive greening may be caused by insufficient light.

Yucca elephantipes Spineless Yucca

Positioning: Maximum sunshine; in a cool sunny room close to a window in winter (minimum 5°C/41°F).

Season: Foliage all year.

Height: Up to 2m (6½ft).

Spread: 90cm (3ft).

Care: Keep fairly moist from spring to autumn; let compost dry between waterings. Very little water in winter; none if kept at 5°C (41°F). Apply fertilizer every 4–6 weeks in spring, summer to mature plants that are repotted every 2–3 years, none required for smaller ones that are repotted annually. Repot in spring in well-drained soil-based compost in deep containers. Lower leaves wither naturally; leave to dry before removing.

Propagation: Pot up offsets.

Recommended: Basic species only; *Y. aloifolia* and *Y. a.* 'Variegata'; *Y. gloriosa* 'Nobilis' and 'Variegata'.

Useful tip: Mature plants may flower outside in a sunny place in summer.

YUCCA ELEPHANTIPES

Unmistakable and dramatic, yuccas can live for years if treated with care, gradually developing into stately and slightly exotic palm-like trees. This species does not have spiny tips and is the best choice for a large room or hallway; try propagating several cuttings in one pot to create a magnificent clump.

Zantedeschia Arum Lily, Calla Lily

ZANTEDESCHIA 'BRIDAL BLUSH'

These are handsome lilies with large bright spathes, like a single petal, that can reach 23cm (9in) long. The foliage is arrow-shaped and lush, as might be expected from marsh plants: try growing them beside an indoor swimming pool or in a cool conservatory, where plants can grow into large robust clumps.

Positioning: Good light while flowering; some sun; but not at midday.

Season: Flowers spring and early summer.

Height: Up to 90cm (3ft).

Spread: 60–90cm (2–3ft).

Care: Gradually increase watering from the time leaves appear in autumn and keep moist until flowering finishes; then reduce and allow to dry out for 4–6 weeks. Feed with fertilizer weekly in spring, early summer. Repot in late winter or late summer; or top-dress large plants by replacing the top 5cm (2in) of compost. Keep cool from autumn until flowering starts.

Propagation: Divide the rhizomatous roots at repotting time.

Recommended: Z. aethiopica, Z. a. 'Green Goddess', 'Crowborough', 'Little Gem'; Z. elliottiana; Z. rehmannii; 'Black-eyed Beauty', 'Harvest Moon', 'Maroon Dainty', 'Shell Pink'.

Useful tip: Repot Z. elliottiana in mid-winter.

80